To my parents,

Without your support, love and guidance, none of
what I have accomplished would have been possible.

-Saverio Scheri

The Casino's Most Valuable Chip

How Technology Transformed the Gaming Industry

2115 Edgewood Drive
Palo Alto, CA 94303 USA
Telephone: (650) 857-0765
Email: john@historytech.org

Publisher: John McLaughlin
Author: Saverio Scheri
Company Profile Author: Charles Anderer
Project Director: Gina Woolf
Art Director: Keith Costas
Photo Editor/Archivist: Sally McBurney

First Edition

Library of Congress Catalog Card Number: 2001096087
Scheri, Saverio 1966–
Anderer, Charles, 1949–
ISBN 0-0640217-8-2

Published in Palo Alto, California, USA
Printed in Hong Kong

The Casino's Most Valuable Chip

How Technology Transformed the Gaming Industry

Acknowledgements

The Institute for the History of Technology would like to thank the following companies for their generous support as sponsors:

3M Touch Systems
Avero, Inc.
Bally Gaming and Systems
Barona Valley Ranch Resort and Casino
BMM Test Labs
Boyd Gaming Corporation
Caesars Entertainment
FutureLogic
Gaming Standards Association
Gasser Chair Company
Harrah's Entertainment
InfoGenesis
JCM American Corporation
Mars Electronics International USA
Venture Catalyst
WMS Gaming

We gratefully appreciate the assistance of the William F. Harrah College of Hotel Administration. We thank the Gaming Standards Association and the National Indian Gaming Association for their support and guidance. The University of Nevada Las Vegas was an important source of information and photographs.

Thanks also to the following individuals for their assistance and support: Jack Drucker, Patrick Leen, Thomas Nelson, Walter Scott, Robert Stewart, Gary Thompson, Kathy War, Helene Scott and Bill Woolf.

Saverio Scheri would like to personally thank Jim Nickerson (for his exhaustive research), Gail Zalarick, Walt Hawkins, Marshall Andrew, Michael Wood, Joe Basara, and WhiteSand Consulting.

Table of Contents

W 1462

FLAMINGO HOTEL AND
CASINO, LAS VEGAS

I

Las Vegas: New Year's Eve 1946 at the Flamingo

Benjamin Siegel Puts Las Vegas on the Map

On New Year's Eve 1946, people in sharply pressed tuxedos and beautiful gowns wandered into a brand new casino in Las Vegas. Opened just a few days earlier, the Flamingo Casino and Hotel was an oasis in the desert. The dream and vision of Benjamin "Bugsy" Siegel, this casino was unlike any other in Las Vegas. Large and spacious, it was the first incarnation of the mega resort.

While the casino hotel was not quite finished, Mr. Siegel felt it was imperative to have it open for New Year's Eve - one of the most lucrative nights for a casino, even today. The grand opening a few days earlier was far

THE FLAMINGO HOTEL AND CASINO

from perfect. They abandoned a formal dress code at the last minute and confused guests by changing the original opening date from December 26th to the 28th and then back again to the 26th. In the first week it was open, the Flamingo lost $300,000. Two weeks later, the Flamingo closed to complete construction and reopened in March, 1947.

The Flamingo is popularly considered the first casino on The Strip, but actually the El Rancho Vegas predates it by five years and The Last Frontier by four, making the Flamingo the third casino on The Strip. Whether first or third, it certainly was the most luxurious at the time. With the casino looking out onto the pool, framed on either side by three-story hotel room wings, the Flamingo flaunted hot pink leather chairs and dealers in white tie and tails. Bugsy's connections to Los Angeles allowed him to book popular entertainers like Jimmy Durante, Xavier Cugat and his band, Tommy Wonder, Eddie Jackson and Rose Marie, all of whom were on hand for the grand opening.

But as glamorous as the Flamingo was, it didn't have the high-tech computers of today's casinos. The end of World War II brought home thousands of Americans, who started to reinvigorate industry and research in the country - but back then, computers were the size of small buildings. They did not offer much functionality other than basic mathematical calculations, but the thirty ton (yes, 30 ton!) ENIAC computer (Electronic Numerical Integrator And Computer) was very use-

RIGHT: BENJAMIN "BUGSY" SIEGEL

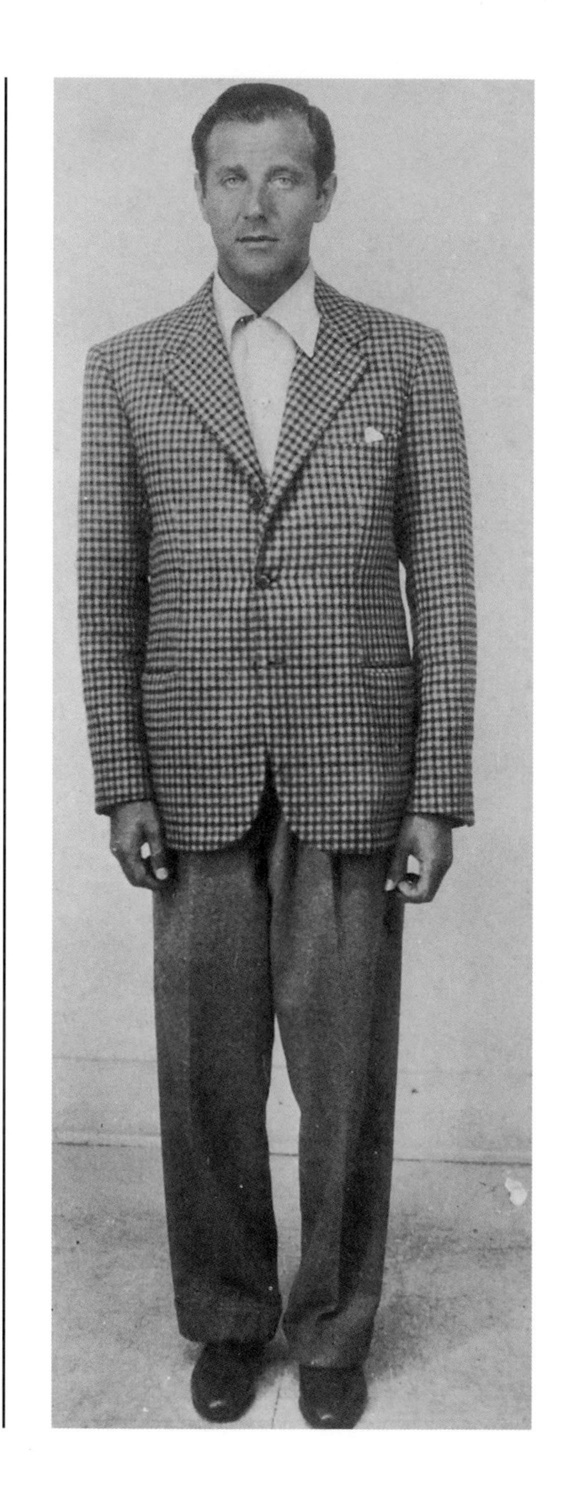

ful during the Manhattan Project to help calculate yields of the first atomic bomb.

As you can imagine, the first casinos did not have any computers to assist in checking guests into the hotel, counting the money from the slot machines or table games, tracking the play of customers, or performing the hundreds of other tasks associated with the operation of a casino hotel. The most technologically advanced devices in the casino at that time were actually the slot machines, and even they were just mechanical devices - a far cry from today's popular sensory experience of lights and sounds.

Golden Nugget

During the early days of the Flamingo, computers were not the necessity they are today. Checking in at the hotel was fairly simple because the volume of people was not nearly as high as it is today. When the Flamingo opened, it had only a fraction of the rooms it has now; today it has over 3,700. The casino was smaller as well, with just a few slot machines compared to today's several thousand. Although the record-keeping was manual and labor intensive, it was not as prohibitive as it would be today. The large resorts in Las Vegas today would not be feasible without sophisticated computers to help manage the hotel and casino. Imagine trying to check-in 5,000 guestrooms at the MGM Grand on a Friday night without a computerized hotel system. It would take all weekend!

It would be more than twenty years before computers became practical in medium-sized businesses like casinos in Las Vegas. The first computers weren't seen in casino hotels until the mid-

1970's, and even then, their use was minimal. Casino owners and operators were understandably reluctant to embrace computer technology. The high cost of the technology and limited functionality didn't seem to justify the expense, so many resisted using computers for as long as they could. As shocking as this may seem, some casino owners continued their resistance through the 1990's, providing the bare minimum of technology needed to run their casino, and failing to update the technology with newer, faster systems. This tactic had a negative impact on their operation, putting their casino at a competitive disadvantage.

"Why don't you play some twenty-one, on the house?"

Modern casinos have thousands, sometime hundreds of thousands of regular players. The largest gaming corporations with many casino properties even have millions of different customers in their database. Tracking these customers is obviously a task that only computer technology can perform.

In the early days of casinos, there were far fewer customers in the casino, so it was easy for a sharp casino manager or pit boss to keep track of them manually. Most of the time, he knew the high rollers by name and would recognize them whenever they came to the casino. Based on his knowledge of how much money a particular customer would potentially put in play in the casino, he could make decisions about how to reward or entice that player. A high roller could expect free meals and rooms, like many high rollers in Las Vegas today, but they might also receive a stack of chips from the casino manager to play "on the house." This was a common enticement for many high rollers during a time when casino chips could be used to pay for things anywhere in the casino, and could even be used to gamble in other casinos.

The extension of this credit to customers was not even written down. Often, a smaller chip would be placed in front of the player indicating they owed a certain amount back to the casino which could be repaid in chips or cash. Sometimes it was paid back in cash, but it often became part of the skim that was rampant in the early days of the casinos.

Las Vegas Wecome Sign

As you can imagine, the lack of tracking and paper trails made it almost impossible for the government to know exactly how much money was being made by the casinos, creating a hotbed of opportunity for criminal activity. Money skimming, fraud, money laundering, and a host of other crimes were much easier to perpetrate without computers to track the myriad of transactions.

The early days of gaming in Las Vegas, a time that many remember fondly and yearn for, were quite different than the Las Vegas of today. Today, on a busy Saturday night, it can sometimes take longer to drive down The Strip than it does to drive through Manhattan. Even with over 130,000 hotel rooms, you can still find the town sold out on certain weekends, and wait times for valet parking can be twenty minutes at some larger properties.

In the early days of Vegas, it was much different. You could drive up and down The Strip without any traffic at all. Although there were just a fraction of the hotel rooms there are today, you could usually find one on a Saturday night. You didn't need valet parking, because there was usually parking available right in front. The marketing strategies were quite different as well. The task then was to attract people to Las Vegas - the task today is to attract them to your casino. Las Vegas has become one of the most popular destinations in the United States, attracting more than 37 million visitors each year - second only to Disneyworld. The task is no longer attracting people to Las Vegas - that has been accomplished. The competition between casinos has now increased to a point that requires sophisticated analysis of customer behavior that only a computer can perform.

Comps for Customers

While most casinos offer some form of this enticement for gaming play today, it is proffered in a much different way. New laws, regulations and good business sense govern who gets the offers, the value of the offers and how the offers are tracked. Only through sophisticated business systems can casino hotels make sound business decisions about the best use of cash and complimentaries that are provided to their customers. Casino management in the days before computer technology was available was more art than science, forcing casino owners to trust their casino managers in ways that would lead to the near collapse of the entire industry.

RECENT FLAMINGO HOTEL AND CASINO

As the gaming industry continued to evolve and mature, marketing campaigns also continued to advance. This resulted in creating a more sophisticated casino customer that knows much more about entitlements than ever before, and is savvy enough to compare offers.

In the past, free rooms and food were enough to earn customer loyalty. But as capacity grew, with more casinos in the same gaming jurisdiction and casinos built in new gaming jurisdictions, competition intensified. This precipitated a new wave of complimentaries targeting a broader market. Room discounts, comps for slots (including cash rewards), trans-

Interior of Arizona Club
Las Vegas, Nev.

portation comps, discounts on losses, and gifts all became part of the arsenal available to casino hosts.

It Will Take Forever To Count All This Money

After a short, rocky start and the ultimate demise of "Bugsy" Siegel, the Flamingo quickly began to generate substantial revenues. More tourists started to visit The Strip instead of just the downtown area. Better highways, faster trains and more entertainment all contributed to the growth of the Flamingo and other casinos in Las Vegas.

As the success of the Flamingo continued to flourish, other casino hotels were built using the same concept - luxury, glamour and excitement - aimed at attracting more and more gamblers to the casinos. In those days, the food wasn't very good, the hotel rooms were cheap, and most everything was given away for free. It didn't really matter, because the customers kept coming to the casino and playing the twenty-one tables, craps, roulette, and the slot machines. The money really started to flow, especially as advances in air travel made it easier and faster to get to Las Vegas. This made it easy for the casinos to give free rooms and meals to their customers, because the money generated in the casino more than justified the comps as an excellent marketing tool.

LEFT: WHILE GAMBLING HAS BEEN PREVALENT IN NEVADA SINCE THE 1800'S, IT HASN'T ALWAYS BEEN LEGAL. FROM 1861 TO 1869, AND FROM 1910 TO 1931, GAMBLING WAS ACTUALLY ILLEGAL IN NEVADA.

WILDLIFE HABITAT WATERFALL

Counting the money from the casino was no easy task, albeit an enjoyable one. Each slot machine needed to be "dropped." A slot drop was the coins that overflowed from the hopper in the slot machine into a bucket in the base of the slot machine. These buckets were picked up each week or each day, depending on how busy the casino had been. The buckets were transported under heavy guard to the count room. For slot machines, the coins were brought to the "hard" count room, as the money was hard coins. Here it was weighed, counted and wrapped. Some of the wrapped coin was re-circulated back to the casino for change, called "impressments."

Slot machines were not nearly as profitable as table games in the early casinos; most cash was generated at the table games. Money from the table games was collected in a similar fashion, but from "drop" boxes in each table. This is the box underneath the small slot on each

FLAMINGO HOTEL AND CASINO, LAS VEGAS

table that the dealer pushes your money into whenever you place bills on the table. A customer places bills on the table; the dealer exchanges them for chips, and then pushes the bills into the drop box. These boxes were brought to the "soft" count room for counting, wrapping, and re-circulation into the casino. Most of the cash didn't need to go back to the casino; instead, it was ready for deposit to the bank ... or skimmed for payment to organized crime figures that bankrolled the casino in the first place.

Casinos didn't need to "fix" the slot machines or the table games in their favor. There were some greedy casino owners who felt the need to take advantage of their customers, but for the most part, operators kept the games on the level - the odds were always in the favor of the house anyway. So it became that the casinos sold entertainment - the time and experience of playing the game instead of whether the customer won or lost at the game. This would be how the casinos would justify their operation in many ways to many people.

The more the casinos grew, the more customers visited, and the more money the casinos made. The more money they made, the longer it took to count the money. Primitive devices helped speed the process somewhat, but there was still no audit trail to verify the amount of money taken in by the casinos.

MARGARITAVILLE RESTARAUNT AT THE FLAMINGO

Unlike any other business in the world, there was no audit trail; no inventory that needed to be purchased in order to manufacture something or re-sell an item at a mark-up. Instead, casinos basically just collected cash from their customers - no credit cards and no checks - just cash. In exchange for this cash, casino patrons received chips, and a chance to win more chips (again, no audit trail) or lose their chips in the wagers. As you may know if you've ever visited a casino yourself, customers most often left their money behind with the casino.

VINE

II

The Role of Technology and Organized Crime

The Art of the Skim

By the early 1960's, organized crime had a controlling interest in many of the major Las Vegas casinos. In addition to the Flamingo, the mafia had the Desert Inn, Dunes, Tropicana, Aladdin, Sands, Stardust and Riviera in their portfolio. All fronted by "legitimate businessmen," the mob funded their acquisitions and investments from teamster money. The influence of the mob was far-reaching, with crime families from Detroit, Milwaukee, Kansas City, and Cleveland involved, with Chicago and New York overseeing the whole thing. Chicago mob boss Sam "Momo" Giancana was arguably the most powerful mob boss west of

1966 'Hello America' Donn Arden at Desert Inn Hotel

the Mississippi and a frequent patron of the Las Vegas casinos. Sam was kept in check only by Paul Ricca and Tony Accardo, and was rumored to have had a hand in everything from helping to garner votes for John Kennedy to participating in a government plot to kill Fidel Castro. The real money for organized crime came from the skimming of profits from the casinos.

As Las Vegas grew in popularity, so did their coffers. The casinos were generating millions of dollars in revenue each month, but the mob wanted to make their money without having to report it as income and pay taxes on it. While the casinos were fronted by the "legitimate businessmen," they had their inside man work the count rooms. Only the inside man knew how much money the casino actually made each day. The inside man would then skim off the top money to be paid to the various organized crime families based on the percentage of interest. The amounts were staggering: Even in the early 1960's, the skim could run between $300,000 and $600,000–or higher each month.

One of the reasons the skimming took place is that it was very easy to do. There was no technology to thwart or even track the activity in the casino. As money was placed into the slot machines, it filled a small cone-shaped bucket called a hopper. When the slot machine paid off, coins were released from the hopper into the tray. Since there was usually more money going into the slot machine than coming out, the hopper usually filled up quickly and overflowed.

As explained in the last chapter, the overflowing coins spilled out and dropped into a bucket located in the base of the

LEFT: COUNT ROOM

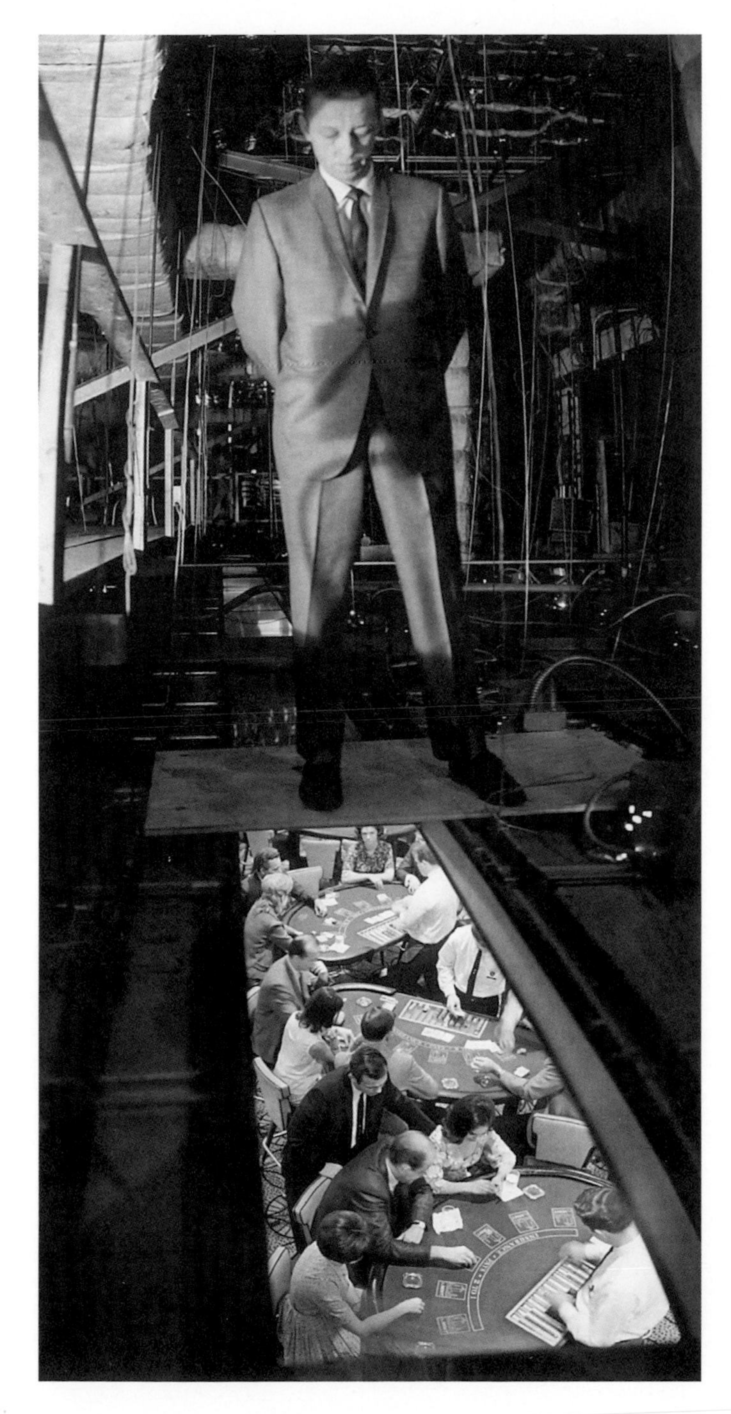

slot machine stand. The bucket was then removed each day or so, depending on how busy the casino had been, and brought to the count room. In the count room, the coins were weighed and then counted and wrapped. In the 1960's, there was no way to audit the counts except by the people in the count room, and they were usually part of the skim or paid off not to notice. The same process was used for the money taken from the tables, except it wasn't weighed; only counted. It was easier to skim the bills, or soft count, than it was the coins.

During this time, there were no surveillance cameras, only people walking or crawling around up in the ceiling on catwalks. It was impossible to watch every game and slot machine. In the count rooms, there were no catwalks, just one person from the Nevada Gaming Board. The skim was easy to conduct, and more profitable than actually operating the casinos legitimately. Each month, trusted representatives from the crime families would travel to Las Vegas–pick up the cash–and bring it back to their bosses. They would carry briefcases and suitcases filled with cash from the count rooms, and no one knew any better. If they did, they were usually on the mob's payroll, so no one talked about it.

LEFT: Casino Catwalk

The following is an excerpt from an FBI report filed in February 1963:

Many of the "Strip" hotel-casinos routinely hide a large portion of their assets. These reported accountings are generally considered to be only 70-80% accurate. (It is very difficult to detect sustained underestimation of taxable income in large cash-based businesses.) Underestimated table profits are estimated to amount to untaxed revenue of over $105,000,000 per year ('62 fiscal estimate). This practice is called the "Skim."

Cash receipts are taken directly from casino counting rooms and dispersed to couriers who messenger the money to pre-arranged spots. Large-denomination bills are substituted for slot-machine coins & daily accountings are fraudulently tallied inside the counting rooms proper. Casino "Skim" is virtually impossible to detect. Most hotel-casino employees subsist on low wages & untaxed cash gratuities & would never report irregularities. This endemic corruption extends to the labor unions who supply the major hotel-casinos with workers.

DEAN MARTIN AT THE MGM GRAND

Skimming was not limited to the count rooms. In the early days of casino gaming, customers received credit with little or no paper trail. During the course of their visit, the casino manager would offer the patron a discount on the money owed to the casino if they paid right away in cash. The credit was paid off for the customer but the cash rarely made it to the cage – it usually went straight to the organized crime families that held percentages of the casino operation. Some gamblers were flown in from New York on junkets. After their trip home they would settle up their losses with organized crime members or associates in New York. Only through wiretaps did the FBI learn of these skimming operations and eventually start to indict some of the players.

The little cash left was used to cover the expenses of the casino such as the payroll, food and beverage, cards, dice and other supply items. Some of the expenses were quite high–entertainment fees for performers like Frank Sinatra, Dean Martin and Sammy Davis Jr. were so high that they even received "points" in some casinos at very low buy-in amounts. Sinatra had nine "points" or nine percent of the Sands, and also received a salary. Dean Martin had one point at the Sands. The casinos also spent lavishly on refurbishing the casino and hotel rooms almost every year, spending so much money that some casinos would even post a loss for the year. This kept the casinos looking beautiful, and reduced or eliminated their tax liability altogether. Interestingly enough, most casinos today continue to reinvest heavily in their properties, updating rooms, carpets, blackjack tables and slot machines as often as once every year or two. But the reasons are very different today compared with the days that the mob controlled the casinos–today it's to remain competitive with all the other casinos that have opened on the Las Vegas strip, a feat that requires significant investment and considerable management skills.

After working so hard for many years to keep Las Vegas under the tax collector's radar, the casinos were now in the spotlight and needed to explain why they were being bought and sold for a fraction of their value. They also needed to explain why organized crime figures were now being connected to the owners and operators of the casinos–and why they were not reporting and paying taxes.

Technology and Regulations Save the Casino Gaming Industry

Many steps were taken to extricate organized crime from the casino gaming industry, including the arrest and conviction of organized crime members engaged in a variety of illegal activities. Corporate investors were lured in to purchase casinos at a price that was far more lucrative than the skimming operations that were underway. Steps were taken to eliminate the corruption that infiltrated the local and state governments.

FRANK SINATRA AS A YOUNG MAN

One of the most important steps taken was to create technology and internal controls to regulate, audit and report on the operations of the casinos. Without the implementation of these controls, and the technology to support them, corporate investors like Howard Hughes would never have been successful in wrestling control of the casino away from organized crime.

The transition was slow for the industry, seemingly taking two steps forward and one step back. Much of the progress was made only when computer systems became widely used in business during the mid-to-late 1970's. Computers that could actually help track revenues were installed in the casinos, along with procedures that were designed to maintain the integrity of the games and money counting operation. Only the combination of regulations and computer technology could help turn the casino industry into a legitimate and respected industry.

HOWARD HUGHES 1947

By the mid 1980's, much of the organized crime presence in Las Vegas had been dramatically reduced. Many of the original owners and operators were either dead or in prison, and casino gaming companies were going public on the New York Stock Exchange. While organized crime's presence had been reduced, it certainly was not eliminated. In 1984, the Stardust was given the highest fine in Nevada's history–$3 million for illegal skimming. The operators were put in Nevada's Black Book of "excluded persons," rendering the Stardust rudderless. The Gaming Board approached Sam Boyd, the owner of the well-respected, family-run Boyd Gaming Corporation to request that he operate the Stardust until a suitor for the property could be found. After taking on this challenge for eighteen months, Boyd was able to reduce expenses and create an efficient operation. In fact, it was so efficient, that Boyd became the suitor and purchased the Stardust in 1985.

The advances in technology, along with the creation of internal controls and procedures designed to protect the integrity of casino operations, were the catalyst to restore public confidence in the casino gaming industry. Bringing in trusted operators, respected publicly traded companies, and the watchful eye of an honest Gaming Control Board worked to rejuvenate casino gaming and spur a new era of expansion and growth.

SAM AND BILL BOYD

One of the technological advances included the installation of surveillance cameras throughout the casino. This not only included the table games and slot machines, but also the casino cage and the count rooms. In addition, the cameras were connected to VCR's, allowing the activities of the day to be recorded and reviewed at a later time if necessary. This provided the ability for the surveillance team to be small and focus on key events throughout the day, without compromising the surveillance of other parts of the casino. This played a huge role in eliminating the skim operation in the casino count rooms.

Additional technology that helped eliminate the skim on slot machines was the advance in the machines themselves as well as a computer system that connected all the slot machines. One of the advances in the slot machines was incorporating electronic meters that counted every coin going into the machine, every coin that went into the hopper, every coin that went into the drop and every coin that was paid out to the customer. These electronic meters were read manually every day by the casino slot drop team, which also included members from security and a gaming commissioner, providing a further check and balance. The electronic meters were also transmitted via the slot computer system and printed on reports.

Money collected from the slot machines was brought to the hard count room where it was weighed and counted. A comparison was then made between the electronic meters that were read during the drop, the electronic meters reported by the computer system, the weighed coin and the counted coin. That resulted in no less than four checks and balances. Each of the four numbers from each slot machine was printed on a computer report and sent to the commission. The totals for each slot machine had to match in order for the commission to approve the drop for that day. As time progressed, the skimming was eliminated and the casinos were no longer required to conduct a slot drop every day, nor read the electronic meters. The computer systems had become reliable enough that the meters were approved by the commission on a daily basis, while electronic meter reads were still conducted once a month. This procedure is still in effect today.

Stopping Organized Crime Today

Vowing never to have organized crime control casinos again, state regulators and casino operators have continued to develop new technologies and procedures to protect the integrity of the games, the customer and the casino. Reports from slot machines have become much more accurate, and now some table games can be tracked electronically, reporting the chips that are added to the table as a fill, the chips that are removed as a credit and even the chips that each customer bets. Customers can no longer receive credit without verifying their identification and signing their marker–and it is all verified electronically on the casino's computer system.

Organized crime syndicates, both within the U.S. and outside the country, continue to create new ways to cheat casinos out of their money. While technology and internal controls have done a great job to maintain the integrity of the casino operation, the games and casinos remain vulnerable to would-be cheats and con-artists. The casinos use technology to remain vigilant and protect themselves from criminals that would try to cheat at the casino games or perpetrate other fraudulent scams. Unfortunately, technology is a double-edged sword, as the criminals also use technology to commit their crimes. It is a continuous game of catch-up as the casinos buy new technology to thwart the criminals, and the criminals work to find a way to beat the technology. And with the pervasive expansion of the Internet, there come new threats–hackers, identity theft, viruses, data theft and electronic fraud.

Casino operators, regulators, bankers and the authorities have done an admirable job at removing organized crime from within the casinos, but not entirely from the gaming industry. Organized crime moved from the casinos to the businesses that service them, charging for protection, or owning the companies themselves and charging excessive prices to the casinos. Regulators have attacked this problem too, requiring any company that does business with the casinos to become a registered vendor and undergo a background check that can be as extensive as those for actual casino employees. The reason they can do this quickly and effectively is because of the technology that tracks known criminals and provides information to law enforcement officials conducting the background checks.

Regulation of Gaming Technology

by

Patrick B. Leen & Thomas C. Nelson

The history of gaming technology regulation largely parallels the remarkable evolution of the slot machine. The slot machine was born in San Francisco, grew up in Chicago and reached adulthood in Nevada. It started out as a completely mechanical device housed in cast iron and evolved into a solid state, computer driven cacophony of dynamic sound and dazzling visual effects. A sideshow for much of its history, it has charged past the traditional table game mainstays to dominate the gaming floor in the typical modern casino.

As the popularity, cash flow and technological complexity of slots grew, regulators took notice. It was no longer a simple matter for gaming agents to look at a machine and assess whether it was operating fairly, or had been compromised by an unsophisticated cheater. The development of the stepper gear, virtual reels, coin and bill acceptors and hoppers challenged regulators to develop methods for testing, approving and monitoring increasingly more complex gaming devices that contained integrated mechanical and electromechanical hardware.

As recently as a mere five years ago, the then current gaming technology and the integration of management and audit functions were not even required in some jurisdictions and largely untested where they were mandated. In addition, most gaming devices were developed, engineered and tested predominantly as stand-alone units with basic on-board computer systems that directed the diverse functions of the slot machine. All memory was stored in EPROM and was relatively easy to test and regulate. Today, the current class of gaming devices submitted to the labs from most manufacturers is designed to be incorporated in a sophisticated and diverse plan or gaming concept that incorporates off-site or remote game download capability, with high-density graphics and surround sound. This "state of the art" technology is tied to cashless gaming in a plethora of possible incarnations with ever more sophisticated on-line systems offering seemingly endless monitoring and audit capabilities. Finally, all memory, game function, and most other sensitive game operations are now generally stored on hard drive DVD or flash card media.

The regulators attacked this problem on two fronts. First, they established gaming laboratories to test devices prior to placement in the casino. Second, they developed sophisticated techniques for verifying that the gaming devices actually in use in the casino were the same one that the laboratory had approved for play.

Gaming Device Testing Laboratories

The need for testing labs as part of a government protection model of gaming regulation is obvious, since ". . . no single casino may be capable of testing equipment or games sold by distributors to assure that they cannot be manipulated or cheated to the operator's detriment. Equipping and maintaining a lab and employing trained personnel would be too costly for a single casino." Anthony N. Cabot & Louis V. Csoka, The Games People Play: Is it Time for a New Legal Approach to Prize Games?, 4 Nevada Law Journal, No. 2 (Winter, 2003/2004), p. 254.

All government gaming laboratories test devices against technical standards adopted by the jurisdiction in question. The technical standards are benchmarks ensuring that each device approved for play meets specific minimal requirements. Technical specifications involving randomness, control programs, error detection and meters are relatively standard across gaming jurisdictions.

Governmental Laboratories

Governmental laboratories must inspect and test any electronic gambling device that may appear on the casino floor. In New Jersey, for example, engineers and statisticians focus on: (1) testing the game itself to make sure that it operates

GAMING LAB

correctly according to the manufacturers' design and according to New Jersey statutes and regulations, (2) testing the game to make sure its integrity and security cannot be compromised whether an attempt is made from the inside of the game or from the outside, and (3) evaluating whether a game is fair to the patron. Engineers and statisticians also analyze and test all peripheral components such as bill validators, coin acceptors, coin hoppers, progressive game components, and electronic funds transfer systems. Rich Williamson, manager of the New Jersey lab, feels that "regulators should facilitate advancements in technology when innovation is not an immeasurable threat to gaming integrity. The security of any gaming operation is not dependent on any one element but by systems and procedures of internal controls. The most effective manner for regulators to readily assess risk of threat to the revenue stream or operational integrity is to recruit qualified personnel with specific knowledge to evaluate each proposal.

Government laboratories have pioneered creative approaches to device testing. The Nevada laboratory, for example, was responsible for development of the field trial. After initial successful testing of the device in the laboratory itself, a limited number of games were authorized for placement and operation on the floor of a designated casino. A typical field trial lasted for approximately 3 months unless severe problems prompted early termination. The results of game play were recorded and carefully analyzed by laboratory staff. If the game survived the on floor trial, the laboratory would recommend it for approval.

Private Testing Laboratories

There are several private firms that offer game testing services in the United States. Private test laboratories typically operate either as independent contractors for regulatory agencies who have outsourced testing services, or where the regulatory agency has issued some type of certification indicating that it will accept results of tests performed by the private laboratory. In either case, the device manufacturer compensates the private laboratory for the testing. The degree of state review and reliance on test results from private laboratories varies by jurisdiction.

In recent years, the role of private testing laboratories has become more prominent with the expansion of gaming in tribal jurisdictions and states offering riverboat style casino gambling.

Hybrids

The Division of Gaming in Colorado established the Emerging Technologies (ET) section as its technical oversight body for all issues related to gaming device and system technology. Several technical specialists within the ET section comprise the Systems and Machine Approval Committee (SMAC), which specifically oversees the approval of the electronic gaming devices and associated monitoring systems. The Division has a contract with a private laboratory to perform analysis and testing of all slot machines, component parts, software, and related systems before they are used in Colorado. The private laboratory reviews the results of its tests (including statistical probability analysis, theoretical hold, and security) with the Division's Systems and Machine Approval Committee before issuing its approval of the equipment it tests. If either the private laboratory or the Systems and Machine Approval Committee find fault with any aspect of slot machine hardware or software, the private laboratory notifies the manufacturer to correct the fault before the hardware or software can be released for unrestricted use in Colorado casinos.

Ray Cherhoniak, manager of the Emerging Technologies section, believes that, "regulators should maintain a fair and equitable balance between the development of new gaming technology and the associated regulatory compliance. Also, as new technological advances continue to be introduced into the gaming industry, regulators should strive to maintain a technically proficient and highly trained professional staff to facilitate the industry in providing a fair, honest and secure product for use by the public."

Field Inspection

A key component of a credible regulatory effort is an effective electronic gaming device (EGD) field inspection program. An EGD field inspection program is simply a means of verifying that the gaming devices on the casino floor are identical to those that have been approved for play, and that no unauthorized alteration of these games has occurred. The inspection program will also verify that the devices are properly communicating with the online slot monitoring and accounting system. When this type of program is conducted on a regular basis pursuant to standard protocols, it provides an assurance to both the regulators and the gaming public that the machines are functioning in a fair and honest manner.

Storage media verification and sealing - this is the heart of the field inspection program. It assures that the software approved by the testing laboratories for play is the one actually installed on the machine. Sealing, or placing heat sensitive evidence style tape over the storage media after verification, is a means to prevent, and detect, tampering efforts. This approach is critical since the most famous slot scams in gaming history have involved reprogramming, or "gaffing," of game computer chips after games were approved for play and placed in the casino.

Bi-Directional Testing - an online system is only as good as the data it collects. Inserting coin or bills in a machine and then checking to see if the events were recorded on the system assures that the device is communicating properly. The standard communications check is the so-called "ten-coin test," which, as the name implies, involves running ten coins or tokens through a machine and then comparing noted game activity with the on line report.

As noted, storage media verification is the core of the field inspection program. As slot technology has moved from exclusive use of EPROM computer chips for software storage to hard drives, DVDs and CD-ROMs, the methods for media verification have been required to adapt. The fundamental processes and procedures, however, remain the same.

There are two basic methods of software verification: encryption and binary image. The first involves a comparison of a digital signature embedded in, or generated by, the software being tested with the known signature of the approved software. The second involves a bit-by-bit comparison of the entire software code contained on the storage media with a copy of the approved software. The primary practical difference between the two methods is speed. The encryption comparison can usually take place in a minute or less, while the binary method can take as long as 10 minutes depending on the processor speed of the test equipment. The trade off is that binary comparison provides 100% certainty that the code on the tested program is identical to the approved program. Encryption methods, though extremely secure, could - at least theoretically - be defeated by an astute, knowledgeable programmer.

Even with the fastest, most proficient verification methods, it obviously takes time and resources to field check every gaming device in a large casino. Once the initial verification is completed, however, it is only necessary to test devices when they are changed out or otherwise modified. Otherwise, random testing based on a statistically valid sample is adequate to verify continued compliance.

Summary and Conclusion

Slot history also confirms that old proverb that the more things change, the more they remain the same. Even though the complexity and sophistication of slots has increased over the years, the fundamental regulatory issues remain the same. The machines must function to produce a fair and honest result and incorporate security measures that can effectively thwart the dishonest.

"Thomas C. Nelson and Patrick B. Leen are former state gaming regulators. They are now principals in Gaming Regulatory Consultants, LLC, which provides consulting and training services related to electronic gaming device regulation."

1 Erasable Programmable Read Only Memory. An EPROM is simply a computer memory chip that stores the game program on the motherboard of the slot machine.

Boyd Gaming Corporation

www.boydgaming.com

The personal touch was a critical part of the casino industry's success throughout the 20th century. Even today, as technology assumes a greater operational role, the best companies stay in touch with their roots and constantly place customer needs at the forefront of significant technological investments. No company embodies that spirit better than Boyd Gaming.

FREMONT HOTEL AND CASINO, DOWNTOWN LAS VEGAS

With 18 properties in six states, Las Vegas-based Boyd Gaming is one of the most diversified companies in the business, coming a long way since co-founder Samuel A. Boyd arrived in Las Vegas with his wife Mary and son Bill in 1941 with $80 in his pocket.

Starting out as a $6-a-day casino employee, Sam—whose name now appears on Boyd's three Sam's Town casinos in Nevada, Louisiana and Mississippi—was eventually able to take small ownership positions in the Sahara and the Mint in the 1950's, and open the Eldorado Casino in Henderson in 1962. By 1974, father and son—who remains chairman—had formed the Boyd Group, renamed Boyd Gaming when it was publicly listed on the New York Stock Exchange in 1993. The company, which had already earned a customer-friendly reputation, was also building a record of corporate and community citizenship that would eventually serve as a model for the casino industry as a whole.

Boyd Gaming's growth has also been aided by a philosophy that strikes a balance between centralized management and significant autonomy at the property level. This is a matter of necessity, as Boyd's portfolio includes properties as diverse as the California Hotel and Casino in downtown Las Vegas, which derives 70% of its customer base from the Hawaiian Islands and its joint venture in Atlantic City Borgata, an East Coast megaresort. And there is Boyd Gaming's investment in the Las Vegas locals market, which accounts for half of its 18 casinos, which doubled in size in 2004 with its $1.3 billion merger with Coast Casinos.

TREASURE CHEST CASINO, KENNER LOUISIANA

Senior Management, 1989

Boyd has used technology to promote best practices and optimize results. The company has aggressively built a first-rate infrastructure designed to support intra-property communication and overall profitability. The company has invested heavily in Voice over IP technology to support audio and video conferencing, real-time voice and data reporting, an analysis interface network that allows for enterprise-wide sharing of information, automated service request processing and invested in gaming and non-gaming systems upgrades across its properties.

Boyd also has the distinction of operating what is widely recognized to be one of the most technologically advanced properties in gaming, Borgata Hotel Casino and Spa, a 50/50 partnership with MGM MIRAGE. Borgata's many technological innovations can be traced to Bob Boughner, the property's CEO, who started with Boyd in 1976. During the run-up to Borgata's opening in July of 2003 and thereafter, Boughner and his team applied advanced and creative technological solutions to every aspect of the business to create a competitive advantage that the property enjoys to this day.

The Borgata is a high-tech answer to a basic question that one Boyd or another has been dealing with for more than six decades : How do you keep customers and employees happy?

The answers included a portal designed expressly to handle the huge volume of job applications; upon hiring each received a private voice-mail box and e-mail address. The casino's 3,600 slot machines all used ticket-in/ticket-out technology-making Borgata the first-ever megaresort to open with a totally cashless slot environment. Systems that track activity in the 2,000-room hotel, 11 destination restaurants, 11 retail boutiques, a 50,000-square-foot spa, and the 125,000-square-foot casino were integrated. With the help of customized business intelligence solutions, Borgata's decision-makers use real-time information on the full spectrum of customer behavior to devise timely and innovative approaches to player rewards. In 2004, the casino received the *Larry Cole Award for Excellence and Innovation in Gaming Technology*, proof that another big gamble had paid off for Boyd Gaming.

The Orleans Arena, Las Vegas

Blue Chip Casino and Hotel, Michigan City, Indiana

BAR
7
BAR

EARLY SLOT REPAIR

III

The Evolution of the Slot Machine: From Spinning Reels to Video Screens

From Mechanical to Digital

The first slot machine was invented by Charles Fey in 1894 at his workshop in San Francisco. He created many innovations for coin operated gaming devices, including the original three-reel "Liberty Bell" in 1898.

Considered the first true slot machine, the mechanical Liberty Bell had three spinning reels each with twenty symbols. This design eventually evolved into the microprocessor controlled five-reel device with hundreds of symbols. Originally installed in the Flamingo to entertain the wives and girlfriends of the high rollers at the tables, the one-arm bandits continued to grow in popularity each year, but it took decades for slot machines to reach the popularity of table games. It wasn't until the mid 1980's when the revenue generated by slot machines in the casino equaled the table game revenue. Helping to bolster the popularity of slot machines with casino managers was the fact that they could run twenty-four hours a day, seven days a week, 365 days a year – and they didn't require the cost of hiring dealers. By the 1990's, slot machines were generating between 70-80% of all casino revenue. Some smaller casinos in Las Vegas became "slot joints," offering no table games at all.

One of the reasons slots have gained so much popularity is that they can be played at a slow or fast pace and require minimal input from the player. Unlike table games like blackjack, where players need to add up the total of their cards and make a decision before other players can act, slots require no interaction with a dealer and no math. For a generation that grew up with video games, it's been a natural migration for younger players and an easy attraction for seniors who may not be comfortable playing live table games.

There are many types of slot machines, and some of the most popular are progressive jackpot machines. Progressive jackpot machines link slot machines together with a very small percentage of every coin contributed to a super jackpot. The more slot machines linked together, the larger the jackpot. Linked slot machines can be in one casino or include many casinos. The multi-casino progressive slot machine jackpots can be worth tens of millions of dollars. One of the largest progressive jackpots ever won was almost $200 million.

A distributor for Bally Gaming in the 1970's, Si Redd championed the spread of the dollar slot machine. In 1980, he invented the video poker machine, and when Bally executives passed on the idea, he took the patent and a 10-year exclusive out on his own. He joined forces in Reno with a company called Fortune Coin to form a new company called Sircoma. Sales for video poker slot machines started to take hold, especially in Atlantic City, and in 1981, they went public as International Game Technology (IGT). IGT then bought the rights to a novel electronic stop for reel slot machines that allowed them to create exciting, new slot machines such as *Double Diamond* and *Red, White and Blue* which are still very popular today.

The original mechanical slot machines had three reels controlled by a number of gears and levers. When the player pulled the handle, the reels would spin and a braking system would stop the reels in a random configuration. If the symbols lined up, coins were paid out to the player. As anyone that has played a slot machine knows, the symbols don't line up very often.

Electrical slot machines eventually replaced mechanical slots, but the basic

2ND COIN WINNERS
5,000
500
2000
200
ANY ONE
WINNERS
5000
600
240
200
160
80
INSERT BILLS BELOW
PAYLINE
WINNER PAID
CREDITS
$1
THIS MACHINE ACCEPTS
$10 $20 $50 $100 BILLS
Insert Bills Into Slot
SEVENS
7
UP
ACCEPTS
100 BILLS

Bally Manufacturing Corporation

The original Bally Manufacturing Corporation was founded by Roy Moloney in early 1932 when Bally's original parent company, Lion Manufacturing, established the company to make pinball games (the company took its name from its first, highly successful, game, dubbed "Ballyhoo"). The company, based in Chicago, quickly became a leading maker of the popular games. In the late 1930's, Moloney decided to begin making gambling equipment, and had great success developing and improving the modern mechanical slot machines that formed the backbone of the nascent gaming industry.

After a wartime foray into manufacturing munitions and airplane parts, Bally Manufacturing continued to produce innovations in both pinball and slot machines through the late 1950's, and also designed and manufactured vending machines and established a coffee vending service. Roy Moloney died in 1958 and the company foundered briefly; amid the financial failure of parent company Lions Manufacturing, Bally was bought out by a group of investors in 1963. Through the 1960's, Bally continued to dominate the slot machine industry, cornering over 90% of the worldwide market for the machines by the end of the decade.

In the late 1960's, Bally became a publicly-traded company and went on an acquisition spree, buying several companies including a German game company and Midway Manufacturing, an amusement game company who made coin-operated electromechanical devices as puck bowling games. In the 1970's, Midway would become a primary source of income for Bally as it became an early arcade video game maker and obtained the licenses for two of the most popular video games of all time, *Space Invaders* and *Pac-Man*.

In the late 1970's, Bally made an unsuccessful attempt at getting into the casino business as Atlantic City legalized gambling; this effort was thwarted when the company was unable to attain a permanent license for the completed casino.

By the mid-1980's, the company again was flush with cash and management envisioned re-defining the manufacturing business as a far-flung leisure industry giant. The company began buying other businesses including the Six Flags amusement park chain, the Health and Tennis Club exercise chain and a maker of exercise equipment. The company also was finally successful in purchasing several casinos, including the MGM Grand Hotel in Las Vegas and the Golden Nugget in Atlantic City. This buying spree quickly took its toll on the company finances, however, and Bally was soon forced to sell off several divisions, including Six Flags and the original pinball division. The pinball division was acquired by Williams Electronics in 1988. The Aladdin's Castle chain of game arcades was sold to Namco in 1993.

In 1990, the struggling company was taken over by financier Arthur Goldberg who re-christened it Bally Entertainment, Incorporated, and focused on the health club business and spun off the manufacturing-related parts of the company as a separate division. By 1992, this manufacturing division, Bally Gaming International, had been completely divested from the parent company (licensing back the Bally name). The health-club divisions of the company would go by the name Bally Health and Tennis and later Bally Total Fitness. Many casinos worldwide would take on the Bally name in the maze of ownership and licensing agreements typical of that business.

Source: Wikipedia

concept remained the same. Instead of using gears and levers to spin the reels, a motor started the reels spinning, but decisions for payouts still required the symbols to line up. Reels were stopped using solenoids instead of braking used in earlier generation slots.

Today's slot machines look similar, but work very differently from the older machines. Modern slot machines are controlled by a computer chip, with every pull being random. The computer uses step motors to start and stop each reel at a specific point. The computer drives the step motors by using digital pulses of electricity. (Fluctuating electrical current drove the motor in previous generations of slots.) The digital pulses move the motor a set increment or step, providing precise control over the starting and stopping of the reels. A random number generator (RNG), used for each pull of the slot machine, determines where the reels should stop. These computer chips can be modified to adjust the slot machine odds which affects how often players will

Early Slot Machine

Golden Nugget Slot Machine

win small and large jackpots. This is how casinos can control the hold percentage of the slot machines (typically between 1-14%). The computer chips give the casinos better control of the payouts while keeping the games fair for the players.

The programs contained in the slot machine microcomputers are Electronically Programmable Memory called EPROMS. They provide attributes about the game and instructions for utilizing the random number generator (RNG). These instructions provide the code for slot machines to achieve a certain payback percentage – the amount of money eventually paid out by the machine. Payback percentage ranges are set by state regulators and allow casinos to set slot payouts within those specified ranges. The ranges vary between jurisdictions and are usually between 84% and 99.9%.

Video Poker

Video Poker machines came on to the casino scene in the 1980's, when slot machines started using digital technology and video screens. Some of the first slot machines to use video screens merely emulated spinning reels, devices which became very popular as Video Lottery Terminals (VLT's). Video Poker machines are quite different from traditional slot machines and are even classified differently. Slot machines are considered a game of chance; once you pull the handle (or press the button), the decision for the outcome rests with the slot machine and the player cannot influence the outcome. Video Poker, on the other hand, is considered a game of skill; after the first five cards are dealt, the player decides which cards to hold (if any) and draws new cards to try and improve his or her hand. A player who holds a jack and a queen and then draws another jack will win his money back on a jacks-or-better machine. A player who holds a five and a seven and draws a jack will not win. It earns the designation of a game of skill due to the ability of the player to influence the outcome after the initial deal.

Video Lottery Terminals

Video Lottery Terminals (VLT's) have fast become the newest savior in the gaming industry. With a modest start in various U.S. and international jurisdictions, VLT's have come a long way from their meager Class II beginnings. In the late 1980's and early 1990's, these machines were bad video games with ticket dispensers, and most customers didn't care for them. It seems now they were years ahead of their time, with the rapid deployment of ticket-in/ticket-out machines and multi-line video slots throughout the nation finally happening.

VLT's have indeed come a long way from their beginnings, now completely indistinguishable from actual slot machines – so much so, that many anti-gambling activists cry foul and claim they are slot machines. But clearly, while the look and feel may be slot machine, the underlying technology truly is lottery.

The biggest difference between slot machines and VLT's is how and where the win or lose decisions are made for each event (an event being a single spin on a slot machine or a game on the VLT). A slot machine is a completely independent device, with a computer chip (EPROM) that has a random number generator (RNG) that determines the outcome of each spin. Although slot machines are usually connected to a computer system, it is merely to transmit machine and customer data to make reporting and marketing easier. All game decisions originate and terminate at the slot machine.

On the other hand, Video Lottery Terminals do not possess any functionality to decide the outcome of a game at the machine. All VLT's are connected to a central computer system in which players compete with others for a piece of a pool. Each player is assigned a number in pools that have predetermined winners and losers. The games are constantly being opened and closed, appearing seamless to the players. The event originates at the machine, but the decision is made at the central computer system and transmitted back to the machine. Also, VLT's are video (hence the name), while slot machines may be video, spinning reels, or a combination of both.

There are a number of companies that manufacture VLT machines and systems, including IGT, Bally Gaming, GTech, Spielo, Aristocrat, Intralot, Williams, and Video Lottery Technologies. Not surpris ingly, many of these companies also manufacture slot machines, allowing them to create VLT's that look and feel identical to slot machines – an important factor in making VLT's as popular as the slot machines they mimic, and consequently, driving similar revenue.

VLT's started in small jurisdictions with a strict limit on the number of units installed, but have rapidly expanded throughout the U.S. and around the world. Currently, VLT's are installed in nine states in the United States. Keeping in mind that thirty-eight states have legalized lotteries, there continues to be optimism for more expansion.

VLT expansion in the U.S. may have the best future in the racing industry. As horse and dog tracks continue to watch revenues siphoned off to other disposable income venues, they are desperate for a B12 shot in the arm. With competition from traditional gaming jurisdictions, Indian casinos, on-line wagering, and simulcast, on-track revenues have been steadily declining. But many states, including Oregon, Delaware, Iowa, Louisiana, Rhode Island, and most recently New York, have looked to VLT's to help bolster their racing industries. Other states are now watching very closely to determine the success of these endeavors, with the hopes of replicating the winning formula in their state. Most notably, Florida, Texas and New Jersey are on the cusp of passing legislation that will allow VLT's or actual slot machines at their tracks.

This, however, has sparked even more litigation both for and against the expansions. Casinos in New Jersey seem to be terrified at the prospect of VLT's or actual slots at the Meadowlands (nearby to their most profitable market) – so much so that they have offered to collectively pay the three tracks in New Jersey $86 million NOT to install any type of gaming machines. The casinos have also discussed the possibility of leasing the racetracks themselves, allowing them to operate the machines and maintain their customer base. All this is still less than they think they would lose if the legislation were ever passed and the casinos were left out in the cold.

Internationally, VLT's are enjoying continued expansion with similar numbers, but in a different way. Most international installations have many fewer machines than a U.S. installation, but there are many more venues. VLT installations are quite pervasive in many countries throughout Europe, South America, Asia, Africa, and Australia.

A number of different variables will play a role in the future of VLT's, especially here in the United States. First and foremost is, of course, politics. As more states look to new revenues for taxation, gambling is always attractive. It usually means high revenues to tax, and no impact on state residents. Some states have gone a little too far with this premise, creating tax structures as high as 50% and 70%, making it nearly impossible for any company to operate successfully. But as states look to invigorate racing in their state and fund important backyard projects, VLT's will continue to play a role and expand beyond their current installation base.

Internationally, the proliferation of VLT's will continue to rapidly expand. As more countries migrate to casinos that look and feel like U.S. casinos, larger venues with more machines will be desired by patrons, helping to drive demand for VLT's and traditional slot machines.

Another key factor in the future role of VLT's is the technology itself. Many slot machine manufacturers are moving toward downloadable, server-based games, allowing operators to change games, denominations, hold percentages and bonus points from a centralized computer system, on the fly. VLT systems would already have the infrastructure to provide similar functionality relatively quickly, assuming regulators approve the concept. This will make VLT's and their technology infrastructure very attractive to racetracks, lotteries and even some casinos, as the concept of downloadable games gains support with gamblers. But keep in mind, some gamblers may become very wary of these types of games, realizing that operators can change hold percentages on a whim, without their knowledge. The manipulation of the game, whether perceived or real, will certainly affect play levels on the downloadable, server-based games.

1960's TV Sitcoms Meet Casino Gaming

As the popularity of slot machines began to dominate the revenue producing portion of the casino floor, slot manufacturers worked to continue creating new and exciting slot products. Empowered by new technology in the 1990's, it allowed them free reign in their creations; they looked to develop novel concepts that would engage customers and have them play longer. Dramatic departures from the traditional slot machines failed miserably. Even minor changes affected productivity and revenue of the machines. Manufacturers slightly changed the size and shape of the cabinet in which the slot machine was housed, and players abandoned the machine, resorting back to older versions that felt familiar and comfortable. More dramatic changes like all video were taboo. Manufacturers realized quickly that they had to move slowly in order to bring players along with their plans for the future.

One of the first developments that slot players embraced was chairs! Believe it or not, there was a time when only a few slot machines had seats in front of them. Keep in mind slot machines were originally designed to be a minor diversion for the wives of "serious" gamblers. But as their popularity grew, casino operators wanted to make slot play as comfortable as possible. The next widely accepted revolution was the slant top machine. The slant top looked like the original stand-up slots, but its design made it easier and more comfortable for players as they sat to play. Clearly, the early focus was on the ergonomics of the machine, and not the game itself.

Players initially resisted video poker machines, even with their liberal payback percentage of 95% or higher in most casinos. But as they caught on, other types of video slots were slowly accepted as well. Video slots that emulated spinning reels finally started to become accepted by the players, as they made the play session more exciting even animating the symbols on the reels. This gave way to re-introducing an old concept with a new twist: nickel slot machines with multiple paylines – as many as fifteen, with a max coin as high as forty-five. Very quietly, nickel machines had the capacity to be more profitable than quarter machines, allowing up to $2.45 per spin.

Players grew tired of staring at cherries and bars all the time. They needed something to renew their enthusiasm, and consequently, their contributions to the casino. Slot manufacturers responded by licensing some of our most beloved televi-

Slot Machine Interior

sion game shows and sitcoms like *Wheel of Fortune, I Dream of Jeannie,* and *Bewitched.* Their popularity was enormous, and broke open the flood gates for more licensing such as *Price is Right, Munsters, Adams Family, Austin Powers, Clint Eastwood, Saturday Night Live, Blues Brothers, Who Wants to be a Millionaire?, GameMaker, Blazing 7's, Monopoly, Jackpot Stampede,* and *Reel 'em In.*

But not all slot machine themes are a hit with players. Almost 50% of the games introduced each year are not popular enough to win favor with players and fail to generate the required revenue to stay on the casino floor. That's why so many new slot machines are introduced each year. IGT alone introduces anywhere from 40-60 new games each year, hoping that more than half will be winners with the sophisticated slot players.

The success of these new slot machines is tied to both the theme and the ability to utilize digital technology to enhance the sight and sound sensory experience.

While there may be some slot players that prefer the old style of slots with bars and cherries on the reels and coins dropping into a slot tray, the slot machines of today are digital video and use tickets instead of coins.

Bally "Bejeweled" Video Slot Machine

Slot manufacturers already offer slot machines where players can select which video slot game they want to play and what denomination the slot machine should be when they play. They can use tickets instead of cash, and the slot machines interact with players by greeting them by name and wishing them a *Happy Birthday* when they play during the week of their birthday. Slot machines award bonuses to players in ever increasingly clever ways, from celebrities cheering them on to even allowing players to select a random award themselves. Future slot machines will be more than we can dream of today, just as today's machines are a cacophony of lights and sounds that would dizzy players of the first slot machines. Who knows what tomorrow's slot machines might offer players: virtual reality, sight, sound, smell and touch sensations – but you can bet they will be the most exciting presentation of technology ever assembled to entertain gamblers!

Bally Gaming and Systems

www.ballygaming.com

Leadership companies generate strong results and shape markets at the same time. By that definition, Bally Gaming and Systems has repeatedly led the gaming and entertainment business from the 1930's into the 21st century.

As a pinball machine manufacturer, Bally revolutionized its industry by introducing the first game with "flippers." Bally's post-war "Hi Boy" slot machine featured a new electro-mechanical mechanism that reshaped the slot industry. In the 1970's, Bally became the first publicly listed gaming company and created its Slot Data Systems division (SDS), the first fully computerized casino data collection system. Bally also entered the new Atlantic City market with the Park Place Hotel & Casino. Operations would be a major part of the business until 1992, when Bally Gaming International was spun off as a separate company focused on the manufacture of gaming machines and systems.

By this time, Bally had built a game library that included such enduring favorites as *Blazing 7's* and *Black&White*, added video slots, video poker and, in 1994, multi-game touchscreens to its list of innovations. The company merged with Alliance Gaming in 1996, and it subsequently embarked on a series of strategic technology acquisitions. By 2004, Richard Haddrill, chief executive officer, could quite credibly say, "We now have the broadest technology for the gaming industry of any company."

The company's prime asset is a flexible and integrated menu of games and supporting technologies, giving Bally an unsurpassed ability to respond to a growing spectrum of player tastes and operator demands for efficiency and marketing power. Licensed game themes, such as *Playboy, SATURDAY NIGHT LIVE, ATARI Pong*, and many other well-known brands are enhanced by such technologies as a wide-area linked progressive jackpot system and Alpha, a video gaming platform displaying advanced graphics and offering a heightened level of interactivity. A hybrid version of Alpha combines traditional reel-spinning slots with interactive video in the same box, injecting new life into established brands.

Bally's future growth will flow largely from the higher-

RIGHT: "BLACK & WHITE" SLOT MACHINE

margin systems side, where its slot accounting and players tracking products have a 40% share of the North American market, and are used by over 300,000 machines and 225 locations worldwide. The company invests an impressive 10% of total revenue in technology R&D. Results include the in-house development of eTICKET, a suite of cashless gaming solutions—which was expanded from 20,000 machines to 125,000 machines in the 2003-04 period—and iVIEW, an interactive LCD touch-screen slot display, a groundbreaking CRM technology that enables slot players to review their club points, dining and entertainment options, or request a casino host. On the acquisitions front, Sierra Design Group (SDG), a supplier of games and systems technology to the growing Class II Indian gaming and state-run central-server video lottery terminal markets, was purchased in 2004. The SDG system, already in place in Washington, Oklahoma and Florida, is at the forefront of the move toward server-based gaming, which enables operators to manage game features and content from a central location.

Also acquired were Casino Marketplace, a slot promotions tool that adds bonusing and promotional functionality to the eTICKET system; MindPlay, a system that uses state-of-the-art optics to bring player tracking to table games; Advanced Casino Systems Corporation (ACSC), which broadened the slot management capability of SDS; and two European slot and casino management system providers, Honeyframe Systems and Micro Clever Consulting, which added to the considerable global marketing potential of the systems division.

For Bally, whose progress has long been an integral part of the gaming industry, the future will resemble the past. "We are extraordinarily well-positioned to lead the industry in the years ahead, as systems and game technology converge, and as technology becomes an even greater driver in casino profitability," said Haddrill.

LEFT: "BLAZING 7'S" SLOT MACHINE

Gasser Chair Company
www.gasserchair.com

A chair is not just a chair. Ask any casino operator.

In gaming, the chair silently welcomes you to a slot machine or table game. It is where you sit, stretch, fret, exult, eat, drink, win and lose for perhaps hours at a time. Full-scale casino resorts number thousands of chairs, representing a significant capital investment. Chairs must be comfortable, durable and functional. And they must accommodate the many quirks of the gambler, making casino seating an art form unto itself.

One manufacturer has been dedicated to this discipline more than any other: Gasser Chair Company. Gaming is about 50% of Gasser's overall production, and the company estimates that it earns a 40% to 45% share of the gaming seating market. All told, the company offers over 100 different chair designs to the gaming industry.

Three brothers, Louis, Roger and George Gasser founded the company in 1946. From the beginning, they established a reputation for sound engineering, innovative product design and application, and careful attention to detail and service.

A consistently innovative company, Gasser was the first to design and develop a unique style of aluminum framed seating specifically for the hospitality and entertainment industries. Aluminum, which was considered a Space Age material of sorts back in the 1950's, is highly durable and lightweight, two attributes that made the material a perfect fit for casinos. Other developments over the years include the first flexible backrest, consisting of an aircraft alloy aluminum bracket that connects the seat to the back of a chair. Gasser was also the first to advocate casters and swivels in hospitality seating; today, most casino seats have a swivel. In the mid-1970's, George Gasser designed and patented a specially extruded vinyl plastic edging called the "Protective Edge" on its entire product line, a feature that has been indispensable to the company's success in the hard-use environment of 24-hour gaming establishments. Modular construction makes it easy to remove and replace damaged or worn parts, and to refurbish chairs once the five- to seven-year furniture life cycle has run its course. Barring an unusual catastrophe, Gasser's products can almost always be stripped down and re-conditioned.

Gasser Model GEO44-017-072

For all of its technical proficiency, Gasser's contributions to the casino business are perhaps best explained by its unique focus on gaming. The company started supplying products to casinos in the 1960's, when George Gasser started working with industry legends Bill Harrah and Harvey Gross in northern Nevada and Si Redd in southern Nevada.

"When the business was very small, there were not too many companies interested in making products that were specific to the gaming industry, meaning the proper seat heights, the proper widths and depths needed to be functional," said Mark Gasser, executive vice president, who forms part of the second generation of Gasser family management that now guides the company.

The company enjoys a deep understanding of the casino industry, how it operates and, most important, how players behave. For instance, gamblers have a unique relationship with their seat, one that has a direct impact on design.

"When a slot player enters a casino, their focus is to win and be entertained," explained Gasser. "We've found that many slot players at first don't sit down—they'll make their first couple of wagers standing. When they do sit down, they'll often sit sort of halfway-on and halfway-off. So we have to make a seat that will accommodate these various positions—one knee on, one off, and so on-and provide a feeling of relief once they finally do sit back in the chair and take the weight off their legs. The function of sitting down needs to be comfortable.

"Also, if you make the stools too wide, and you can't get in between them, you make it very difficult to draw the player in. They're unable to get in between the stools without competing for floor space."

Gasser Chair has consistently responded to changes in player tastes, game design and player demographics. An aging customer base in the slot area, which now typically accounts for 60% to 70% of overall casino revenue, has created the need for an ergonomically-sensitive chair design, and chairs that can accommodate physical changes in the population.

"In the early days of the casinos, first there were no stools, and then there were stools with no backs," said Gasser. "Now you have stools at every machine because it's accepted that seating improves slot revenue production. The customer is much more likely to stay if they're able to sit down and rest while they're playing. So stools have a backrest and more attention is being paid all the time to the ergonomic properties of the products. We make people more comfortable with a scalloped seat and with a back that has some type of a lumbar support."

Gasser also deals with a fairly wide variety of operator views as to what constitutes the cor-

TREASURE CHEST SLOTS

rect or best seat height. There are some who feel that a higher seat height, such as 27 inches, which is typically used at a blackjack table, is better because it allows a player to look directly at the reels of a slot machine. Another camp believes a stool should be as small as possible so that nothing interferes with the glass of the machine or any other game design aspect that draws players in. Then there are those who feel that making people climb up into a stool is less inviting than having them sit down in a stool.

"This is something we're going to all have to consider as the population ages, and we have to deal with more and more elderly players," said Gasser. "The larger trend is toward a 24-inch and lower seat height. In working with some of the larger slot manufacturers, there is a definite move toward a 22-inch seat height-both with and without footrests."

The rise of branded slots has led to the demand for design elements on the back of slot stools to extend the marketing impact of a given game, such as branded slots like *Monopoly* and *Men in Black*. More and more casino operators are finding that it's worth the cost, when you're talking about a $12,000 to $15,000 gaming machine, to extend its reach by putting signage or logos on the back of the stool. High-limit areas have grown in popularity and in size. Those areas may have been 10 or 15 machines in the past. Now, there can be 200 or 300 machines of the higher denominations.

"Operators certainly recognize and are willing to pay more for an upscale stool for those machines, because they want customers to see that there's a difference in that area," said Gasser. "Even if they don't use a larger or more comfortable stool, they may use genuine leather, some type of velour or a decorative embroidery."

Larger body sizes of players, as one might imagine, are affecting the course of Gasser's production and design. The company regularly accommodates requests for large or oversized stools, and it produces stools with no arms on them so a larger person won't feel "pinched" or uncomfortable. Operators, for their part, are beginning to recognize the need to space slot machines further apart. "We can only make the stool so wide if we're not increasing the amount of space between each machine," said Gasser. This strategy is becoming more prevalent in highly competitive markets, such as Las Vegas and Atlantic City, two places, like many others in the business, that feature thousands of Gasser chairs.

BMM Testlabs

www.bmm.com

The pace of innovation continues to grow exponentially in gaming, particularly on the slot floor. The sheer volume of new games and systems puts enormous stress on regulators, who must first evaluate and test the underlying technology in order to guarantee the integrity of the product to the general public.

A handful of the largest gaming jurisdictions in the United States – including Nevada, New Jersey and Mississippi – have state-funded laboratories for this purpose. But this isn't a practical solution for most commercial and tribal gaming jurisdictions. Hence the rise of an efficient outsourcing option, the independent testing lab, in the 1990's and into the early part of the 21st century.

BMM Testlabs is a key player in this market. Established in 1981, BMM has a staff of over 60 engineers worldwide, in offices that stretch from Sydney to Nevada to New Jersey and from South Africa to London. An ISO 9001 and ISO 17025 certified company, BMM is an Accredited Testing Facility according to the Australian scheme for certification of independent testing facilities for gaming and wagering systems.

BMM's Australian roots are significant, as the firm cut its teeth in New South Wales, where, in the early 80's, it worked closely with a division of the Totalizator Agency Board (TAB) to develop an operating system for that state's slot market. "New South Wales is probably one of the most mature gaming markets in the world," said Paul Miller, Director of Marketing and Sales. "They've been operating slot machines for well over 60 years. They've got 105,000 slot machines, which are all hooked up under one big central monitoring system. At any time they can pull up a report to see what a specific machine is doing in a specific location."

"In 1990, we were also the very first gaming lab to work with downloadable game technology with an operator in Australia," continued Miller. "The Australian market has provided a very significant grounding for us as far as our capability to understand a range of gaming technologies is concerned."

This early focus on systems figures to pay dividends for BMM in the future, as operators continue to push for a more efficient, software-driven operating environment, such as the opportunity to download games from a central server. This transition was already underway by 2003 with the spread of server-based gaming in the Class II sector of the tribal gaming market. No surprise, then, that BMM, which only began operating in North America in 2001, was selected two years later by the National Indian Gaming Commission to help create a set of technical definitions and technical standards for Class II games.

"We have absolutely no doubt that system-centric gaming will transform the slot floor going forward," said Miller. "If you look at the history of the industry, slot machines used to be mechanical devices with a pull handle on them. Today, your average slot machine has the processing power about 4 to 5 times larger than a pretty hefty Windows-based PC. These machines are also networked over many types of systems such as casino management systems, marketing systems, bonusing and EFT (electronic funds transfer). In the past, it was a machine-centric world, and the system was just a real-time data collector. But now, things are moving more toward the system having control over the network. Ultimately, I believe it will be one large seamless network, where a lot of the functionality will be server-based."

BMM's job is to certify that gaming machines and systems work consistently and reliably in a way that ensures that customers aren't defrauded and that regulators are able to collect tax. BMM also ensures the security of information. A typical BMM project assignment involves, among other things, conducting a wide range of tests to ensure a game and/or system complies with its specifications and technical requirements, including hardware, system software, application software, data communication, load, restart and recovery, integration, acceptance, security and compliance testing.

In the U.S., BMM's market is divided among three types of jurisdictions: those that have their own, state-based test labs (e.g. Nevada, New Jersey and Mississippi); states that operate commercial casinos, but don't have their own testing lab (e.g. Illinois, Missouri); and tribal casino jurisdictions. Each of these jurisdictions operates under a set of regulations and technical standards, which BMM is equipped to test to.

In the U.S., BMM deals with vast differences in technologies employed, variations on regulations used, and different functionalities allowed for each jurisdiction. Clearly, this all results in different software versions deployed in different regions. BMM tackles these complexities by assembling a unified set of regulations, which it describes as a kind of superset of all different possible regulations. From this vantage point, it can understand the variations employed in different jurisdictions and specific software versions.

It can be said that independent labs meet a need created by the lack of technical standards and regulatory consistency between jurisdictions. This is a reflection of the vast political and commercial differences that exist between gaming markets.

"Major jurisdictions such as Nevada and New Jersey have major operators who want everything based on opportunity and cost," he said. "I've heard it said that they would like everything to be 100% reliable, 100% of the time, infinitely expandable and backward compatible. That's the sort of thing that they're striving for which is, of course, impossible to achieve. If you take a jurisdiction like Mississippi, which is only 10 years old but which has 29 properties, they do things on a free-enterprise model. They regulate how and where and when a casino can operate, but they don't regulate the particular validity of each operation; they stand on their own merits. On the other hand, new jurisdictions spring up with pro- and anti-gaming constituencies and very specific regulations have to be written for political reasons. Given all the different pushes and pulls of the political landscape, it's virtually impossible for one jurisdiction to completely adopt another jurisdiction's approach."

The value of BMM to the gaming industry is perhaps never more clear than when a critical new technology such as ticket-in/ticket-out (TITO) hits the market. TITO is the method by which tickets, or transportable vouchers, have replaced coin-based gaming. The opportunity to both grow revenue through ease of play and reduce costs by making the slot floor less labor intensive proved irresistible to operators across the North American continent. Each jurisdiction had to test the technology itself, as well as its ability to interface with a broad range of supplier product. The resulting workload was too much for state labs to handle on their own. Nevada turned to BMM to assist with TITO testing. And Mississippi used BMM exclusively in a pilot program to test TITO systems as well. At the time, BMM had 60 engineers; 15 of those in its Nevada office. The state lab of Nevada has about half-a-dozen engineers; Mississippi has three or four.

BMM's future success hinges on its continued investments in technology and human capital, and on the drive by governments to stay lean and flexible, even as gaming expands. The firm's engineers typically have 10 or more years of experience, and hold either an electrical engineering or computer science degree. They are also required to have previous involvement with gaming, be it at the manufacturer or operator level. BMM also maintains multiple versions of all existing commercial systems and runs and inter-operates these systems with all the different slot platforms.

"I don't know of any gaming manufacturer or any state-based lab, outside of maybe Nevada and New Jersey, that has a copy of everything," said Miller. "I don't know of too many other institutions that run that whole infrastructure and that have a full understanding of inter-operability and communications. We have a unique skill set because we operate at the intersection between gaming technology, gaming operations, and regulatory compliance."

JCM American Corporation

www.jcm-american.com

No history of gaming technology would be complete without a note of gratitude to JCM and Aki Isoi.

As head of Osaka-based Japan Cash Machine's (JCM) American office, Aki identified gaming as a potential market for the firm's currency acceptors. In 1988, he sold operators in the Atlantic City market on the idea that slot play and overall operational control could measurably increase if players were able to deposit paper money instead of coin into a machine.

Studies would subsequently show that machines with acceptors outperformed those without by 30%. And JCM's creation of the embedded currency acceptor with a lockable and removable cash box in 1992 added security and integrity to slots. By 1994, it was rare to see a slot machine without JCM's product. The company would go on to enjoy a decisive (95%) market share, a dominant position that it maintains through a combination of strategic and technological vision.

WBA GROUP

ONE MILLION WAREHOUSE

A supplier to the world's leading slot manufacturers, which compete on a global scale, JCM developed in 2004 its Universal Bill Acceptor (UBA), which accepts all currency up to 85mm in width. The UBA uses magnetic and optical sensors for a more complete and secure bill scan and is packaged with a durable plastic 500-note capacity cash box that contains an on-board memory feature that independently records each transaction.

JCM is also bringing revolutionary change in table games. In 2003, it introduced embedded currency acceptors to table games, and followed up in 2004 with its Trident system, which uses the acceptor as a platform for real-time data collection in the pit. The system offers ease-of-use for the dealer, and improved security and control for the operator, who no longer have to tabulate results manually. All this with no disruption or change for the players.

None of this was envisioned in the tradition-bound world of table games just a few short years ago. But, then again, no one ever thought players would feed $20 bills into a slot machine.

t Bonus '97
ACCEPTS

10

"QUARTERHORSE" SLOTS IN AN IOWA INDIAN CASINO

IV

Next Generation Slot Machines

Progressive Slot Machines Create Instant Multi-Millionaires

Since the Flamingo opened its doors in 1946, table games had always earned the most money for the casinos. Slot machines held their own in regard to revenues with their low operating costs, but were mostly reserved for the wives of the table games players or the occasional player looking to kill some time. But that all dramatically changed in the 1980's. The changes actually started to manifest themselves in the late 1970's, when slot machines got a new look. By the early 1980's, more and more people were playing slot machines, and casinos took notice. They started working with the slot machine vendors to create more exciting games and larger jackpots. This is about the time slot machines started to look more like the devices we see in today's casinos.

As casino revenue from slot machines continued to increase, the revenue from table games began to decline. Each year, slot machine revenue grew while table game revenue declined. This was not due to table games players switching to slots, but rather table game players dying off (figuratively and literally) and new slot players coming to casinos. Traditionally, table game players were older, male, and veterans of World War II. This is not a hypothesis, but rather a trend identified by the examination of the casinos' customer base. As these customers aged, they frequented the casinos less often, and unfortunately also moved on to that big casino in the sky. As the market base for table games began to change dramatically, so did the market base for slot players. Demographic analysis of customer databases reflected that slot players were originally older and female, but newer, more exciting slot machines, such as video poker, started to attract younger players as well as male players.

Realizing there was an opportunity to radically change the slot market, and subsequently the casino business forever, slot manufacturers created a new technology that linked multiple slot machines together. The unique aspect of this technology was that it not only linked slot machines together in the same casino, but it also linked together slot machines in different casinos. The purpose of linking these slot machines together was to have each slot machine contribute a fraction of the coins played into one super jackpot. This linking of slot machines to a super jackpot was called a wide area progressive link (WAP).

The first company to successfully develop and deploy a WAP was International Game Technology (IGT). This first WAP, called "Megabucks®," was released in

RIGHT: IGT's QUARTER MANIA PROGRESSIVE SLOT MACHINE

March of 1986 and was installed in nine different casinos around the state including Harrah's, Harvey's, the Boyd Gaming properties, and the CalNeva casino, once owned in part by Frank Sinatra.

This was a very exciting time for slot players, as they now had a chance to win a jackpot of at least $1 million. No other game in the world offered such a lucrative payout on every pull of the handle. The first Megabucks® jackpot was paid on February 1, 1987, in the amount of $4.9 million. Walt Hawkins, now over a twenty year veteran of IGT, was an instrumental part of the original Megabucks® team and had the distinct pleasure of providing the check to the lucky winner at the Harrah's casino in Reno.

Surprisingly, the next gaming jurisdiction to install Megabucks® was not Atlantic City — it was Macau. Due to a lengthy approval process in Atlantic City, Hawkins was able to meet with Dr. Ho, the eminent leader of casino gaming in Macau, and secure a deal for

Ticketing System

Megabucks® in his casinos. Megabucks® was installed in Macau in 1988 prior to receiving approval in Atlantic City. Since its debut, many billions of dollars have been won by players on Megabucks® and other WAP links. Bally, Aristocrat, and WMS all offer their own versions of a progressive link, but not before IGT enjoyed almost ten years of exclusivity — not because of a patent or intellectual property, but because no other company could do it at the time. The largest slot machine jackpot ever won (as of this writing) was a Megabucks® jackpot on March 21, 2003, for $39.7 million at the Excalibur Casino Hotel in Las Vegas.

Since its inception, Megabucks® has created over 900 millionaires, and has paid out more than $3.4 billion in jackpots.

Slot Machines Go Cashless

In the early 1990's, the IT leader for MGM Grand, had a novel idea: Instead of slot machines paying out in coins, why not just print a ticket voucher? This ticket could then be re-used in another slot machine or redeemed at the casino cage for cash. While a legal requirement at Indian casinos, this was completely foreign to the slot players of Las Vegas. While most Indian casinos waited patiently for the time they would be able to have real coin play in their slot machines, MGM's IT leader moved ahead with his concept. MGM Grand invested a great deal of money and installed ticket readers on a number of slot machines. The experiment was a complete failure and in the end, probably cost him his job. But he was a visionary — in a short fif-

LEFT: BALLY'S MONTE CARLO BLAZING 7S PROGRESSIVE SLOT MACHINE

teen years, this concept would become all the rage for slot players.

Systems like IGT's EZ Pay™ and Bally's e-Ticket™ now provide the ultimate convenience for slot players: they can insert paper currency into a slot machine, play as much or as little as they like, press a "cash out" button, and a ticket is instantly printed right before their eyes. Customers can then take this ticket and insert it into another slot machine or redeem it for cash at the casino cage or in an ATM-like device on the casino floor. While slot players were not ready for this concept in the mid-1990's, they are embracing it today.

In the past, if you inserted a $20, $50, or even a $100 bill in a slot machine and then decided you wanted to play a different slot machine, you had to cash out in coins. If you had a lot of money still in the slot machine, this could take quite a long time. Then you had to somehow move all those coins from the machine you didn't want to play to the new slot

SLOT TICKETING VOUCHER SYSTEMS

machine. And, when you arrived at the new slot machine, you had to insert the coins one at a time. This slowed down play, and frustrated players and casino operators alike. Tickets made all those problems go away. It even increased revenues, allowing players to play through their money more quickly.

Of course, there are still the die-hard slot players that insist on having the coins drop into the tray and inserting their coins one at a time in the slot machine. They can usually find a few slot machines that will still take their coins, but more and more casinos are becoming cashless — 100% ticket-in/ticket-out. Casinos save lots of money by eliminating all coin from their casinos — no one needs to make change, no one needs to collect it from the slot machines, and no one needs to count it. So they are willing to lose a few die-hard coin players because the savings, along with increased revenues from tickets, more than outweigh that loss.

Since the invention of the transistor, technology has had a profound effect on the gaming industry. From modern slot machines with multi-million dollar jackpots, to customers using tickets instead of coins in slot machines, technology has impacted the games in the casino, and it has also changed the way casinos do business. The impact of these technology progressions can reverberate throughout entire casino resorts, changing casino operations forever.

IGT: An Overview of the Company

IGT ceated and marketed the first video poker machines in the 1970's. The games quickly caught on with players, and IGT adpted the concept to bar-top versions which, in turn, produced new revenue possibilities for neighborhood taverns. IGT evetually sold more video poker machines than all of its competitors combined.

IGT helpd take slot machines into the microprocessor age in the 1980's with the creation of its S-Plus™ spinning reel slot machine. The machine's reliability and serviceability quickly made it the industry standard and led to slot machine revenue eclipsing table game revenue in Nevada casinos. IGT beganintroducing custom game themes for the S-Plus in 1988, and created an average of 25 new themes a year through the '90's. In 2000, the S-Plus™ product line was replaced with the S2000™ slot machine, featuring enhanced audio and visual effects.

About 6 percent of total domestic gaming machines generate recurring revenue, which allows machine manufacturers to participate in the machine's revenue on a percentage or flat-fee basis. Those machines are collectively referred to as "proprietary games" and include linked wide-area progressive systems (or MegaJackpots(SM)) and stand-alone machines. In the North American market, IGT estimaes it holds about 70 percent share of the installed base of recurring revenue machines.

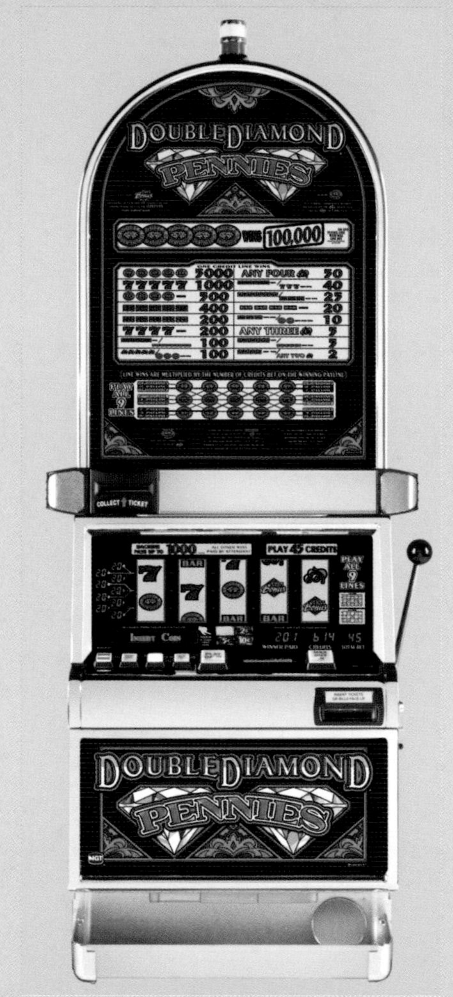

IGT's Double Diamond Slot Machine

IGT operate recurring revenue games in 18 domestic jurisdictions (which includes Native America, comprising 16 U.S. states), plus international markets like Iceland, Italy, and South Africa.

IGT built it reputation on a willingness to customize its products. IGT was the frst company to apply game themes to its slots - something other than a company name or simple denomination on the game glass. Now-classic themes like *Red White & Blue®* and *Double Diamond®* paved the way for hundreds of other slot game themes, and led to the marriage of slots with well-known entertainment and product themes like *Wheel of Fortune®* and *Harley-Davidson®*.

In 1999, IGT unveiled aother gaming machine milestone with its EZ Pay™ Ticket System technology. EZ Pay™ combines ticket printers with traditional hopper pays to improve a gaming machine's cashout function for players. Casino operators can program the machine to pay a portion of the payout in coins and the balance in the form of a ticket. The ticket can be reinserted into other EZ Play(SM) machines; exchanged for cash at a cashier's station; cashed by attendants on the casino floor using wireless validation units; or held by the player for use at a later time. The system can also be programmed to pay out tickets only, using the hopper as a backup. The EZ Pay™ system allows operators to utilize IGT's new EZ Ply(SM) multi-denomination machines, so players may select the game denomination—from one cent up to $25—on a single machine. Players can still insert bills or coins to start playing and can change their wager without the bother of collecting and converting coins when they cash out.

IGT''s *Game King* multi game machine, introduced in 1994, offered just that: a selection of video poker and keno games on a single machine. Players no longer have to move from one machine to another to play a different video game. The latest variation on the theme is the multi-denomination machine, which gives players the option of playing nickel, dime, quarter or dollar credits on a single machine.

In 2002, IGT unveiled anoter major advance in gaming machine design with its AVP™ (Advanced Video Platform) product. AVP's complex, 3D-based games have screen graphics with millions of possible color variations (vs. 256 colors on a standard video slot). It also offers full-screen animation and live video, and greatly expanded game content. The first two machines utilizing AVP™ were *Lifestyles of the Rich and Famous*™ and *Wheel of Fortune® Special Edition*™ *Video Slots Triple Action*™.

The Reel Touch™ Series of slot machines debuted in 2003 and bridges the gap between slots and video games. The machine's touchscreen LCD in the top box adds interactive entertainment to bonus game play, and it's available with an optional EZ Touch™ selectable multi denomination touchpad.

IGT was the leader in introducing slot machines and video lottery terminals (VLT's) into racetracks (often known as "racinos"), pari-mutuels and off-track betting (OTB) parlors. These venues with large clusters of VLT's bring new customers into an existing, regulated gaming environment and generate additional revenues to support racing operations. The addition of machine gaming at racetracks in states such as Delaware and Iowa has saved what was becoming a threatened industry.

IGT now adapts a nuber of the entertainment world's best-known themes to create the most innovative and popular products in its history. Those familiar themes include *Wheel of Fortune®* (the most popular gaming machine in history), *I Love Lucy®*, *ALIEN*™, *The Price Is Right*™, *Harley-Davidson®* and *The Twilight Zone®*. IGT''s original-them successes include *Dragon's Gold*™, *Enchanted Unicorn®*, *Cleopatra®* and *The Frog Prince*™.

IGT was founded in Jauary 1952 as A. Benetti Associates, Inc., which was changed to A-1 Supply in July of that year. In 1971, William "Si" Redd purchased A-1 Supply, Inc. and in 1979 renamed it SIRCOMA, Inc., an acronym for Si Redd Coin Machines. The Company went public in 1981 as IGT, a wholly owned susidiary of International Game Technology, which had an initial public offering that year. International Game Technology was approved for listing on the New York Stock Exchange in January 1991 and became a member of the S&P 500 in August 2001.

Source: Wikipedia

IGT's *The Frog Prince* Slot Machine

WMS Gaming®
www.wmsgaming.com

The slot machine business has thrived thanks to those who dare to change the game. High on the industry's honor roll is WMS Gaming.

The Chicago-based company has played a decisive role in games and entertainment since Harry Williams founded WMS in 1943. A Stanford engineering graduate who devised the "tilt" mechanism on a pinball machine, Williams changed the nature of pinball in wartime America. He and his firm had an unsurpassed ability to devise new game features and stay in touch with the changing tastes of the amusement market. The company retained this inherent strength when it entered the home video market in the 1980's and, eventually, casino-style gaming in the early 1990's.

In its present incarnation, WMS Gaming, with a portfolio that includes many of the industry's most popular and profitable branded casino slots and state-of-the-art gaming technologies, stands as one of the world's leading slot suppliers, with an unmatched reputation for innovative game design and development. However, the journey was not without a few twists and turns.

WMS came to the slot business as Williams Gaming™, developing its first video lottery terminals for the Oregon market in 1992. It entered the reel-spinning market two years later, but the company's video gaming roots ultimately would prove to be its niche when, in 1996, *Reel 'em In®* was introduced to the casino market.

WMS TICKETING COMPONENT

Reel 'em In was at the forefront of a revolutionary movement in the American casino market toward multi-line, multi-coin secondary bonus video slot games. It is nearly impossible to overstate Williams' impact on the overall slot machine business when it merged its innate flair for entertainment with the technical possibilities of video gaming.

Instead of three-reel slots that were confined to 32 physical stops per reel and one payline, games such as *Reel 'em In* have five reels, multiple paylines and up to 90 symbols on each reel. Players can bet anywhere from one to 20 coins-per-line (nickels being the most common denomination), and a winning bet with maximum coin-in qualifies players for a bonus round. The combination of new visuals, player interactivity and new ways to win proved enormously popular. Video slots went from niche status on the slot floor to the overwhelming favorite, eventually relegating reels to minority status on the floor.

More importantly, from the operators' perspective, video slots increase overall win, time-on-device and player satisfaction. Williams enhanced the popularity of *Reel 'em In* with a banked bonus model that added coins to a jackpot collectible only if the player qualified for the secondary bonus screen. Needless to say, this was a powerful incentive not only to keep playing, but also to wager the maximum amount.

Williams leveraged the success of *Reel 'em In* with a string of in-house, multi-line/multi-coin brands that slot players grew to love and which still remain strong earning products several years later. These included *Jackpot Party®*, *Boom®* and *Filthy Rich®*.

The company's growing success in the casino business dovetailed with the decline of the pinball machine industry—which was feeling the effects of in-home and arcade video gaming—leading to the renaming of Williams to WMS Gaming in 1999, a company wholly-dedicated to slot machines.

By this time, WMS was playing a leading role in another transformational movement on the slot floor: the trend toward popular branded games. This involved the adaptation of household brand names to gaming devices. Their biggest hit—indeed, one of the greatest success stories in the history of slot machines—was the introduction of the *MONOPOLY*™ themed series of slots.

When WMS negotiated its original *MONOPOLY* licensing agreement with Hasbro in 1997, the gaming industry was still struggling with the cost side of licensed games. In order to justify the up-front investment in an established brand, slot manufacturers turned to a new leasing model, known as participation. Rising development costs were also a factor, as the games typically included high-value sound and graphics packages, and bonus rounds that resembled film shorts told with dialogue and animation. As a result, the machines were in effect leased instead, sometimes for a percentage share of the net win of the game, a dramatic departure for slot operators, who were used to owning a machine and paying for it in a short period of time.

To justify such a pricing model, licensed games, if they were to be deemed successful, had to outperform conventional games by a wide margin—a rule that still applies. The manufacturer also had to have an understanding of brand development so that the initial appeal of the theme retains its shelf life. When *MONOPOLY* themed slots came along, many slot operators still resisted the participation model. The one thing they could all agree on, however, was that *MONOPOLY* themed slots were worth the investment, because the games consistently out earned non-branded games. Indeed, it can be safely said that the success of the *MONOPOLY* slots helped pave the way for the boom in licensed games that—as in the case of multi-line/multi-coin games—added excitement and an indispensable new revenue stream to the slot floor. The participation model gained in credibility and potential, thus creating a recurring revenue stream for the manufacturer, much of which was plowed back into new licenses and new technology.

The success of the *MONOPOLY* series also validated licensor Hasbro's faith in WMS. "We were first impressed by WMS Gaming's ability to create top-earning products that remain true to the *MONOPOLY* board game, and we are further impressed by the Company's ability to place the gaming machines and their continual efforts to increase the number of units in the field," said Patricia Schmidt, former Vice-President of 3-D Licensing and Promotions for Hasbro, Inc., when the installed base of *MONOPOLY* surpassed 4,000 units. By 2004, there were 14 different versions of the game and over 3500 units installed on casino floors.

As in the case of its earlier video success, WMS was quick to convert its triumph to other branded products. These would grow to include, *HOLLYWOOD SQUARES*™, *SURVIVOR*™, *PAC-MAN*™, and *MEN IN BLACK*™, with many additional well recognized brands such as *POWERBALL*® themed slots to be introduced in calendar 2006. At the 2004 Global Gaming Expo, actor Clint Eastwood showed up in person to support the launch of *A FISTFUL OF DOLLARS*® wide area progressive series, which is shaping up to be WMS' next big hit in the area of licensed brand-themed slots.

Successful new games represent a long-term opportunity, but they also exert new perform-

BLUEBIRD SLOT MACHINE

ance pressures on a slot supplier. At the end of the 90's, WMS was a fast growing company, but one that was also in transition. Creativity in game development is not enough to sustain a slot manufacturer in the 21st century. To build on its successes in the 90's, WMS needed to invest substantially in executive talent, manage technical issues, develop new game technologies and compete on a global scale.

BRIAN GAMACHE - PRESIDENT AND CEO

To this end, Brian Gamache, the company's current President and CEO was brought on board in 2000. A hospitality industry veteran, Gamache brought a deep understanding of organizational development, brand management and sales and marketing to WMS. New technology campuses were built in Chicago and Las Vegas. New sales offices were opened in Spain, South Africa, the UK and Australia. Investments in new technology yielded a new wide area progressive jackpot system, and a new video gaming operating system *CPU-NXT™* with an eye-catching new *BLUEBIRD®* cabinet that won praise throughout the industry.

Gamache was responding to a situation that found WMS with 50,000 machines in the field—the company's stunning successes in the 90's had earned it 18% market share in the U.S.—combined with a gaming platform that was beginning to show the strains of supporting the proliferation of peripheral and complex game requirements. The company's response was to retool the company, even at the expense of new machine sales. While WMS' market share fell to 13% from 2001 to 2003, the company used its strong balance sheet to invest more than $100 million in new technology, infrastructure and new product lines. The investment yielded the Bluebird cabinet equipped with the CPU-NXT platform, named one of the *Top 20 Most Innovative Gaming Products* at the 2003 American Gaming Summit, a state-of-the-art software and inspection system to monitor the integrity of each slot machine, and new game content. The whole package, including new reel spinning, poker and wide area progressive product lines, was ready for commercialization by the fall of 2003.

"Our company had always been very innovative and very creative," said Gamache. "But we needed to invest in the necessary areas that would allow us to accomplish our short term goal of a quick rollout of new and compelling games and our long term goal of becoming the next full service provider to the gaming industry. From the end of 2003 through 2004, operators saw an increase in their earnings from our new content powered by our CPU-NXT operating system featured in our award-winning Bluebird cabinet.

In addition to WMS' popular multi-line, multi-coin, video slots, the company also added mechanical reel slots, poker products and a proprietary wide area progressive system. "We now have the ability to leverage our sales and distribution channels to serve 100% of the casino floor," Gamache said.

WMS also pursued numerous initiatives to bolster internal operations and customer service, including investing in an Enterprise Resource Planning solution that enables the company to automatically update software from a central location to users at its seven U.S. offices.

CPU-NXT is a robustly reliable platform that offers ultra-high resolution video, increased interactivity, unprecedented sprite animation, and superior color capability—it supports a screen of 16 million colors. WMS recruited the best available technological talent to develop the platform, including creative specialists from studios such as Disney® and Sega®. The platform is ethernet-ready, and supports simultaneous hopper and printer, ticket-in/ticket-out, multi-denominational games and progressives. Virtually all of WMS products are upgradeable to CPU-NXT®.

The platform also powers WMS' new Bluebird gaming cabinet. Bluebird features a dazzling ergonomic design, and a technologically advanced video operating system. Its LCD monitor uses an expanded (18.1") digital, high resolution, flat screen with a non-glare display and touch screen capabilities, which is positioned for a better angle in relation to the eyes of the player. The overall appearance is softer than the box-like look of conventional machines, which helps make the cabinet more appealing to female players. Security is enhanced by a sleekly designed coin tray that also serves as a unique anti-theft feature. Because the lip of the coin tray doesn't protrude from the bottom as much as those on other cabinets, it helps minimize the risk of coin theft or outside interference. This gives players and operators—both of whom were consulted during the development process of Bluebird—a greater sense of overall security.

The Bluebird cabinet also features a sound package that is anchored by a *BOSE® FREE FIELD®* directed audio system that immerses the player into the sound of the game with fewer peripheral distractions. The system, which was developed exclusively for WMS Gaming, is equipped with four speakers and innovative directional sound technology, resulting in lifelike sound reproduction similar to that of a live production. With over 80% of the cabinet components interchangeable between the video reel, stepper reel and poker cabinets, and a front door which is split in half, allowing three distinct levels of access to the machine's internal components, Bluebird is also easy to service.

LINE OF SLOT MACHINE MECHANICS

Games remain the lifeblood of WMS, with its investments in technology, the company is positioned to reap enormous benefits from the successes it enjoyed in game development in the 90's. New variations of old favorites using the new platform and cabinet are in the pipeline, including *Jackpot Party Progressive*™, a multi-level progressive, *Reel 'em In Big Bass Bucks*™, *Reel 'em® In Poker*™ and *Leprechaun's Gold® Gettin' Lucky*™. And the company has an enduring flair for combining gaming with licensed entertainment brands.

The migration from the world's leading pinball manufacturer to a world-class gaming machine company appears complete. A strong gaming content company is now a strong gaming technology company as well, with an integrated product offering for the global market.

FutureLogic, Inc.

www.futurelogicinc.com

In the age of cashless gaming, the voucher is king. So it's no surprise that the casino industry has come to depend heavily on FutureLogic, a supplier of thermal printers whose products have grown to dominate an increasingly critical corner of the business.

By 2005, an estimated 70% of the installed base of slot machines in the United States operated on a cashless system. The vast majority of those machines used what is known as TITO (ticket-in, ticket-out), a system that dispenses redeemable bar-coded vouchers. TITO took off in earnest in 2001, when International Game Technology (IGT), the industry's leading gaming machine supplier, launched EZ-Pay. IGT used FutureLogic as its sole source printer supplier for the first three years of EZ-Pay, and the firm remains its primary provider. Today, FutureLogic is the dominant supplier of direct thermal printers in cashless gaming devices with over 750,000 units installed.

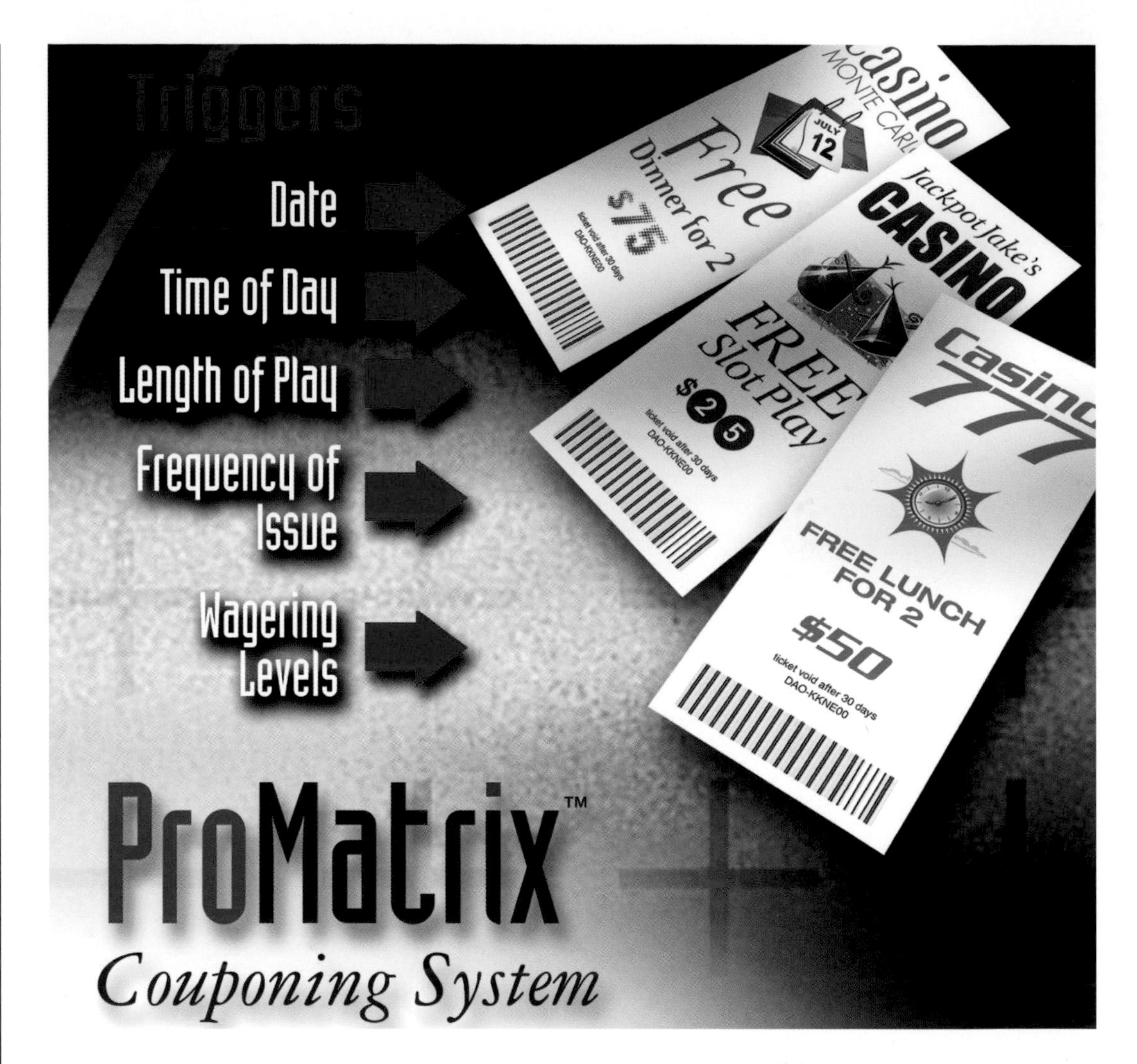

Based in Glendale, Calif., FutureLogic was founded in 1983 by Mark Meyerhofer—now vice president of manufacturing and quality—as an electronics consultancy. In 1988, it entered the field of thermal printer design, eventually supplying the medical device market with printers. Gaming is currently the firm's core business. FutureLogic's printers are used for other transaction-based devices such as gas pump receipts, medical devices, point-of-sale coupons and labels for assembly line products.

Direct thermal printing is extremely dependable—FutureLogic's reliability rates are 99.9%—and efficient. "There are a minimal number of moving parts in direct thermal printing as opposed to dot matrix, or impact printers, which gives the technology a lower operating cost and makes it easier to maintain," said Nick Micalizzi, Vice President of Sales and Marketing "The life span of thermal is longer, and print resolution is superior."

High-quality print resolution is important for two basic reasons: Vouchers use a bar code that must be readable by a bill acceptor. Also, going forward, casino operators are beginning to consider the use of printers as coupon dispensers. This is a convenient and cost effective method for casinos to award free goods and services to attract and retain customers. FutureLogic is well positioned to capitalize on this trend since they helped to pioneer coupon technology in the supermarket industry over 15 years ago.

In the fall of 2002, the company introduced its GEN2™ printer with dual communication ports at the G2E show in Las Vegas. The second port is a dedicated port specifically for system connection and is used to download coupon databases. This next generation printer in conjunction with their patented ProMatrix™ Couponing software includes the support tools and capabilities necessary to make promotional printing a practical reality.

The emphasis on the ProMatrix™ Couponing System requires FutureLogic to work more closely with system providers under various business models to insure a smooth implementation of this couponing solution. "In terms of the casino market, we already have what many people consider the most effective sales force in the industry," said Micalizzi. " The strategy is to call on casinos, present the advantages of our product and create a pull-through, whereby the operators request the OEM's to put our product in their games. It has been a very successful strategy, and it will grow in importance with the move towards couponing. Of course, you also need a world class service organization to support this strategy and we offer that to our customers also."

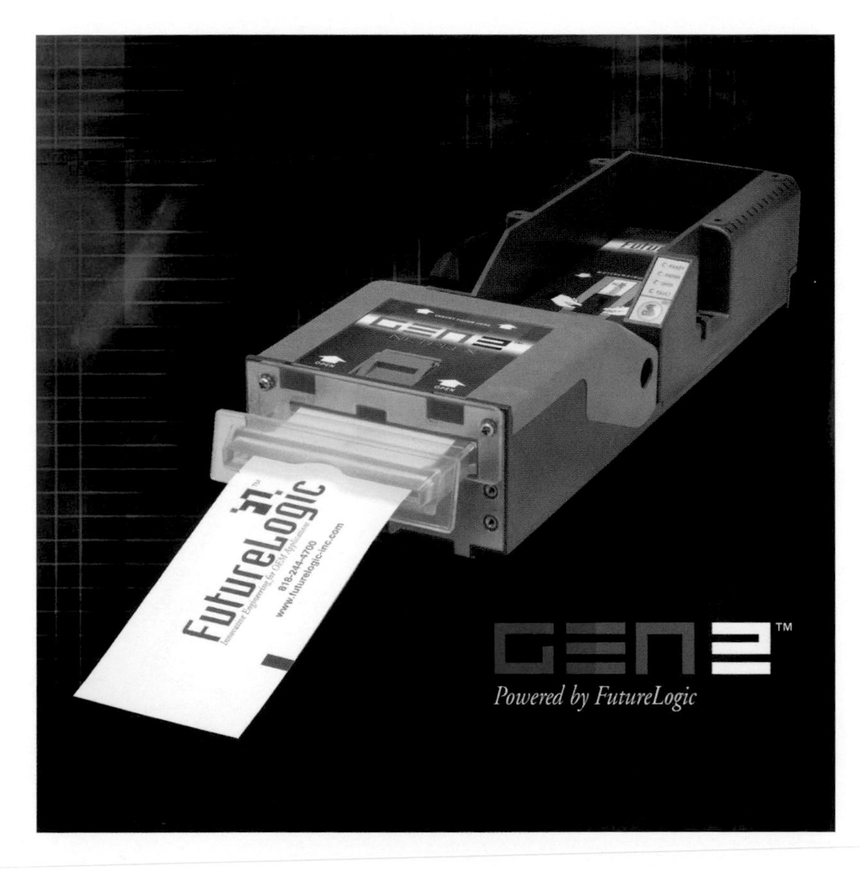

The GEN2 printer family comes standard with 1 megabyte of RAM or an optional 8 megabytes. The Promatrix solution though allows a printer with 1 megabyte to store hundreds of clip art objects which can produce thousands of coupon permutations; more than enough for any marketing campaign. A companion technology, the FlashPod™, a handheld download tool that connects directly to the printer, lets operators download fresh template designs and firmware revisions directly into the printer.

To support the global growth in cashless gaming recent investments include a London office to service all of Europe and Russia, an 11,000-square-foot distribution center in Las Vegas that services the OEM's, a 30,000-square-foot manufacturing facility in Phoenix, Arizona, opened in January 2005, and distributors in Australia and Asia. Logically speaking, the future looks bright.

Patents are currently pending for GEN2, ProMatrix, and FlashPod, among others.

MEI
www.meiglobal.com

The casino business has been built on the non-stop accumulation of huge amounts of cash, and no single product has aided more in this effort than bill acceptors. On the face of it, this wouldn't seem to represent a business opportunity for Mars Inc., the company best known for such beloved brands as M&M and Snickers.

However, MEI, a division of Mars, is a key supplier to the gaming industry whose electronic payment systems handle more than 1 billion transactions per week in 90 countries. By 2004, MEI's fastest growing business segment was gaming, and the strength of its technology had established the firm as a key contributor to the industry's growth and slot segment profitability.

Security and ease of use are two of MEI's hallmarks. The company developed the first electronic bill acceptor in the 1970's. Like every other product on the market back then, early acceptors had limitations. "The acceptor could only read a 1.5 by 6-inch swath of the bill," according to Phil Wesel, Global Marketing Manager Gaming. "Some folks figured out a way to use half of a real bill with a blank piece of paper to get machine credit." Today, MEI's cash-flow acceptors use a five-piece light-bar assembly that maintains uniform intensity of light across the entire path of the bill, eliminating this cheat and many other potential frauds as well.

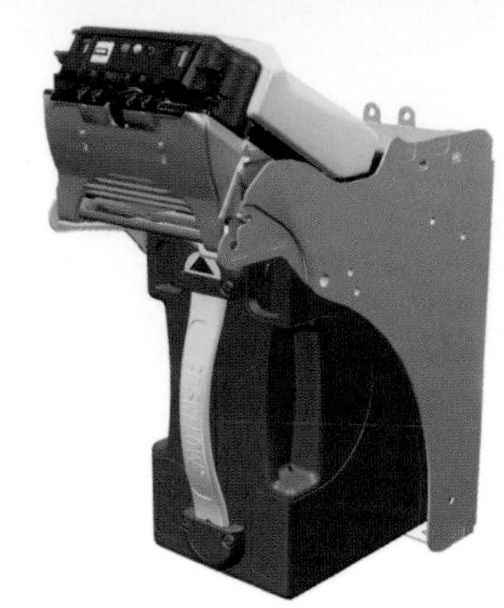
MEI CASHFLOW

MEI also meets the challenges of constant changes in currency. Through the 80's and 90's cheap reproduction technology increased the occurrence of fake notes. Governments reacted by continually changing currency versions and adding design complexity. They added coloration, fluorescent threads, watermarks, and color shifting inks to the notes. A bill acceptor must read all these features except for the fluorescent thread, which is only meant to be picked up by a blacklight.

MEI responded by putting gains in computing power to good use. The firm's first gaming bill acceptor, the GL5, used a 10-megahertz processor. Today's SC-83 Multi-Width is ten times faster. Its predecessor product, the ZT-1200, had four sensors and three wavelengths, meaning it could read 2,000 pieces of data on a bill. The SC-83 has up to 10 sensors and 6 wavelengths, so the acceptor reads 9,000 pieces of data. This particular acceptor can take up to 50 different versions of notes.

The move to voucher-based gaming in 2000, which was fuelled by the rapid growth of ticket-in/ticket-out cashless systems, represented another hurdle. The ZT-1200 was the first product with a bar code sensor in it. As people are not as confident with a ticket as they are with a bill, MEI had to aim for higher acceptance rates.

"If a bill is rejected, you put it in your pocket and walk away," said Wesel. "If your ticket is rejected, you're concerned. The new product advances the technology; we've made the acceptor as forgiving as possible. Tickets can be anywhere up to 5 millimeters from the sensor and it will still read it at 6 inches-per-second." MEI's acceptance rate for tickets is above 99%; anywhere from 92% to 96% on bills is considered adequate.

Low-tech innovations are part of the story. If a player claims they put in a $50 bill and they only got $20 in credits, MEI's acceptors feature a window in the cash box that enables attendants to see the last note or two that was inserted. MEI was the first company to introduce a plastic cash box to the gaming market. These can be dropped 30 times from 6-feet onto a concrete surface and still function.

That's not from Mars, but, like everything else produced by MEI, it more than meets the industry's needs.

a division of MARS incorporated

Avero, Inc.

www.averoinc.com

Food and beverage is big business, particularly on the Las Vegas Strip. The loss leader days of free drinks and meals have given way to expensive foodservice investments and a focus on growing revenues and profits. An important contributor to this evolution is Avero, a company whose web-based software, Slingshot, has given casino operators their first ever F&B business intelligence tool.

Slingshot is the brainchild of Avero's founder and CEO, Damian Mogavero, who got the idea for the company when he was a restaurant group CFO. He found that the inability to monitor server performance and manage costs was an industrywide phenomenon, a discovery that led to the formation of Avero in 1999.

Damian Mogavero, CEO

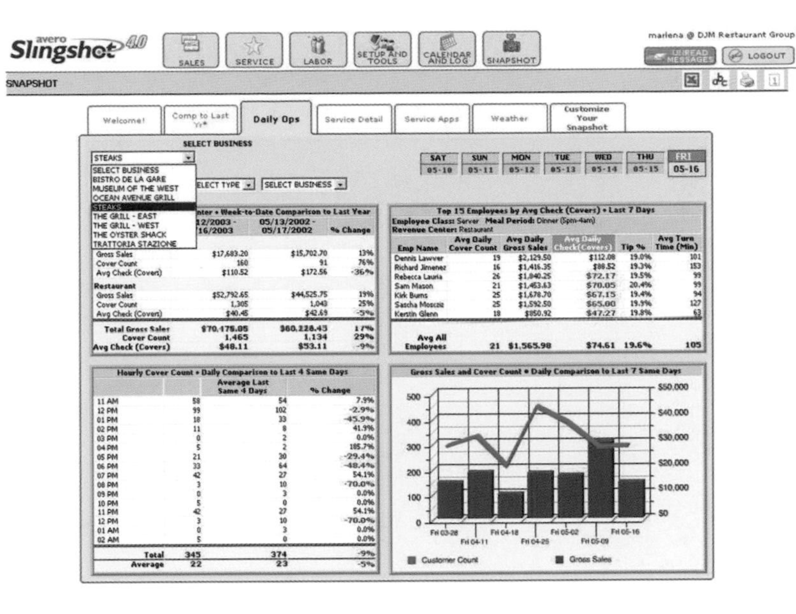

Slingshot Screen Capture

The software, which consolidates transactional data from multiple point-of-sale and time and attendance systems and packages it into actionable reports, caught on with leading chefs and restaurant groups across the country. When Las Vegas came calling on these same chefs, they insisted that Slingshot be part of their operation. From 2002 to 2004, Avero's business grew from zero to over 130 food and beverage outlets on The Strip, everything including restaurants, lounges, room service and the casino floor beverage operations.

The primary benefits of Slingshot are enhanced server productivity, improved cost control, and better customer service. The software gives frontline managers the tools to improve the guest experience. Overall server performance is highlighted, including strengths and weaknesses, with an eye towards improving performance and exceeding customer expectations. Table turn time, the ability to up-sell a customer, response time and cocktail server sales volumes are among the many metrics used.

In terms of savings, Slingshot helps minimize waste and keep menu prices down for the customer. Chefs can review consumption patterns to improve procurement practices. Slingshot also alerts them, through its logbook function, to special events such as conventions that impact demand and employee scheduling. Large-scale customers have significantly reduced labor costs as a result.

Leading gaming companies such as Harrah's Entertainment and Caesars Entertainment have seen gains in profitability following the implementation of Slingshot. With F&B growth in the cards at Las Vegas and across the U.S., Avero figures to be making some history of its own in coming years.

3M Touch Systems
www.3Mtouch.com

For well over a decade, game manufacturers around the world have found touch screens indispensable in providing a richer gaming experience to game players. At present, of all the slot machines that are shipped worldwide, 75% of them have video content. Of those, 95% have a touch screen, according to Dan Savage, business manager, 3M Touch Systems.

3M Touch Systems supplies game manufacturers with ClearTek™ touch screens, the leading touch screen used in the gaming industry today. A capacitive technology-based product, ClearTek™ provides durability, while being very sensitive to the touch. ClearTek™ supports fast game play for expert players, while surviving the harsh environment of a gaming floor 24 hours a day, seven days a week.

Gaming floors are hardly calm environments. Patience can sometimes be in short supply. The repetitive nature of slot play exacts a heavy toll in terms of wear-and-tear on every device. A central question facing touch screen vendors at the outset centered on durability, and this became the primary competitive edge of ClearTek™ capacitive technology.

ClearTek™ capacitive touch screens were introduced to the gaming industry in 1994 by a privately-held firm called MicroTouch. 3M acquired MicroTouch in 2001.

3M continues to invest in the MicroTouch™ ClearTek™ screens, with the newly introduced ClearTek™ II touch screen product. This new product offers excellent light transmission, improved anti-glare properties and great reliability.

On the Road to Success

The road to success began with small video lottery terminal (VLT) markets in Canada and the United States with unique operational requirements. The end result over the years has been massive change on slot machine floors around the world. VLT jurisdictions were set up in the early 1990's as a politically-expedient way to capture gaming revenue without "imposing" full-blown casino development on local populations. That meant putting terminals in places where slot play was not the principal attraction, such as bars, restaurants and race tracks. Strict limits were placed on the number of machines per venue.

Transition for Slot Machines

"Slot machines had been developed as 'button games,' which means they used a micro-switch activated push button," said Vince DiVincenzo, Vice President, James Industries, a longtime gaming manufacturers representative who sells 3M Touch Systems products and worked for MicroTouch during its ascent in the 80's and 90's. "When it became obvious that gaming manufacturers needed to give players more options and expanded content, it became difficult to utilize only mechanical activated push buttons."

"The key dynamic for change became apparent quickly. Instead of having one gaming unit on the floor playing one game in that limited area, the opportunity was to have that box play multiple games," added Dan Savage. "It was very difficult to do that with buttons. You need flexibility to change the format of the games so they could have 2, 3, 5 or even up to 40 games on one machine. The touch screen was the enabling technology that accomplished enhanced play."

A study by gaming analyst W. Bruce Turner of Raymond James, stated that the annual win-per-unit of touch screen games exceeded single-game machines by 40% to 50%, which easily compensated for their $1,500 per-game machine price premium.

The triumph of the touch screen was further validated by a player preference study commissioned by MicroTouch and conducted by Arthur Andersen at the Lincoln Park dog track in Rhode Island, which operated 400 VLT's at the time.

The study focused on the only fully button-capable machine at the track that also had a touch-screen function, thus providing a credible comparison between the two platforms. Among the findings:

- More than 90% of the players started off or selected the game by using the touch screen.

- Changing the amount bet and selecting cards was done by touch 70% of the time.

- Just over two-thirds (67%) played multiple games on the same machine, using the touch-screen to reconfigure the machine to play a new game.

- Those surveyed were experienced with casinos and were dedicated players.

More than 70% of the Lincoln Park study participants had previously played at casinos and more than 60% were going to Lincoln Park on a weekly basis.

The Enabling Technology

Touch screens were the enabling technology and therefore instrumental in the migration from reel slots to video, and from buttons and switches to touch. The rapid acceptance of touch screen technology was about to dovetail with the mid-90's boom in video slots to create a huge new market for touch in conventional casinos, and the Lincoln Park study played a key role, said DiVincenzo. As mentioned above, 75% of all slot games currently being shipped to the casino market now have video content, and all but 5% use a touch screen.

3M MicroTouch™ ClearTek™ Capacitive Touch Screen

What the Future May Hold

The appeal of video touch screen gaming has extended to the table game side of the business, where automated roulette is steadily grabbing market share from the conventional game at casinos around the world.

"That will be a huge opportunity," said Alice Moran, marketing manager, 3M Touch Systems. "As casinos want to expand player access to increase profits, automated roulette and similar games allow you to do that. And the touch screen technology itself is so well accepted by the players today."

Expansion plans for touch technology extend beyond the gaming floor to the casino hotel complex, according to Moran. Many new applications are available for touch screen technology to be used throughout the gaming, entertainment, and hospitality experience at a casino. These include self check-in screens in a hotel lobby, touch-displays on elevators that highlight a property's entertainment options for the evening, purchasing tickets for events, player loyalty kiosks, café table games, interactive menus and even an in-room touch screen display for ordering room service that doubles as a hotel room mirror.

If all that sounds a little far-fetched, imagine what the typical Las Vegas slot manager would have told you 20 years ago if you said "one-armed bandits" would one day be better characterized as video-driven, "one-finger bandits".

CAESARS HOTEL AND CASINO, LAS VEGAS

V

The Birth of the Mega Casino Resort

The Savior of Casino Gaming in the United States

During the late 1970's and most of the 1980's, there was very little expansion of the gaming market in Las Vegas. In 1978, New Jersey legalized casino gaming in Atlantic City, and much of the focus was on the neglected beach resort. In a short amount of time, Atlantic City was generating revenues comparable to Las Vegas with just a fraction of the number of casinos. Located within ten hours driving time of almost 60% of the nation's population (and only three hours from NYC), Atlantic City was perfectly situated for gaming enthusiasts along the eastern seaboard.

For a time, Las Vegas appeared to be dying a slow, quiet death as investments shifted to Atlantic City, Indian casinos, and riverboats. But there was some activity in Las Vegas. A young man named Steve Wynn was buying and selling real estate and was about to purchase his first casino, the Golden Nugget in downtown Las Vegas. He acquired the Golden Nugget, turned it around, and made it very profitable. Wynn did such a great job with the Golden Nugget, that he had investors believing in his vision and his ability to run a profitable casino. So it was easy for them to back his next casino – and it became one of the most profitable in Atlantic City. But Steve Wynn was just getting started – his real vision was for a casino like no other – a hotel that was one-of-a-kind, and a revenue stream that would make the Fortune 50 envious.

BELLAGIO

STEVE WYNN

Like Benjamin Siegel before him, Wynn had a vision to build something in the desert that no one had ever dreamed of before, and no one believed would work. But this was Las Vegas, and history had shown that if it was done right, anything could work. Steve Wynn was about to prove that statement many times over.

The Mirage opened in 1989. At $620

THE MIRAGE

million, it was the most expensive casino hotel ever built at the time. When the Mirage opened, it had over 3,000 hotel rooms and featured a 20,000 gallon aquarium behind the front desk, complete with miniature sharks. With a tropical rain forest theme in the middle of the casino, marble floors throughout, and the Siegfried and Roy showroom and tiger exhibit, this casino was unlike any other in Las Vegas. Oh, and let's not forget the erupting volcano in front of the Mirage that brought traffic on the Strip to a halt every fifteen minutes.

Unlike other casino owners, Wynn was very hands-on. He was involved in almost every decision from the layout of the hotel to the color of the linens. His vision was to create an elegant and excit-

Bergman, Walls & Associates

Bergman, Walls & Associates was founded in 1994 as an architectural firm specializing in resort design, with an emphasis on casino design. Prior to 1994, Joel Bergman spent 16 years as Steve Wynn's in-house architect creating such projects as: the Mirage, Treasure Island, and Golden Nugget in Atlantic City, Las Vegas and Laughlin. Scott Walls was a part of the Mirage organization for the last ten of those years.

During that time, the founding partners' participation in operational decisions provided them an intimate level of involvement to the inner-workings of the hotel gaming industry. It was their architectural end product that introduced a revolutionary new gaming genre to the Las Vegas Strip - the "mega-resort."

ing experience for his guests from arrival to departure – an experience that would leave them exhilarated.

Steve Wynn spared no expense, from the linens on the bed to the custom chairs, from the exotic fish in the fish tank behind the front desk to the marble bathrooms in the guest rooms. Wynn created the ultimate for his high rollers, with magnificent villas that were larger than most people's homes. This watershed event was in and of itself, the single catalyst that spawned a new wave of construction that gave us the Las Vegas we know today. Just like the volcano that erupts every fifteen minutes in front of the casino, the Mirage let loose an eruption of new casino development in Las Vegas.

Rome, Paris, Venice, Egypt and New York City Come To Las Vegas

After the Mirage, Steve Wynn built and opened Treasure Island right next door in 1993. Complete with battling buccaneer pirate ships, it featured a theatrical show with explosions, live actors, and the sinking of one of the ships right in front of the casino several times a day.

Eyeing Wynn's developments, and perhaps envious of his success, other casino companies soon followed suit and began developing their own mega-resorts in Las Vegas. The floodgates were now open. New casino resorts were built, and older properties were expanded – or imploded and rebuilt from the ground up. Circus Circus built the Excalibur and the Luxor, the pyramid shaped casino complete with a life-size sphinx. Kirk Kerkorian, the billionaire who bought and sold the Desert Inn and MGM a few times, built a 5,000 room hotel across the street from the Tropicana on what had been the Tropicana's golf course. The market was so strong that casino companies began to partner with one another, as Steve Wynn and Circus Circus did to build the Monte Carlo casino.

Each new casino resort that opened had to be bigger and better than the last. The

Paul Steelman Design Group

The Paul Steelman Design Group was founded by Paul Steelman in Las Vegas in 1987 – only ten years after graduating from Clemson University and beginning his career in architecture.

His father was a well-respected architect in Atlantic City and Paul worked for his father's firm prior to joining the City of Atlantic City Planning Department. While in the planning department, Paul helped create the Atlantic City Master Plan and realized that entertainment architecture was going to be his specialty. Paul went to work for Joel Bergman and Steve Wynn, and his real learning began with Golden Nugget Atlantic City, Golden Nugget Las Vegas, and other projects. After nearly ten years of working for an inspiring visionary like Wynn, the entrepreneurial bug struck Paul and he opened his own architectural and design practice.

Eighty projects later in 12 countries and 15 states, Paul has completed every type of gaming project including resort, local, European, barge-based, riverboat, pari-mutuel, and Native American. Paul has worked for the Mirage, MGM, Harrah's, Park Place, Harvey's, Hard Rock, Swiss Casinos, Hyatt, Caesars, Sheraton, Grand Casinos, WWF, and many others.

LEFT: BELLAGIO 1998

PARIS HOTEL AND CASINO

properties were becoming "must-see" attractions in and of themselves. New York New York was built across the street from the MGM, with hotel towers that replicated the New York City skyline. MGM eventually bought the property, securing its position on what was unofficially called the "Four Corners" of Las Vegas.

The building boom continued, with Caesars Palace building a new tower and the Forum Shops, a unique shopping mall that re-created ancient Roman streets with high-fashion shops, boutiques, and world renowned restaurants. Created and developed by Dougall Design, the success of the Forum Shops has been unsurpassed, as it continues to generate the most revenue per square foot in the United States, even after three major expansions, the most recent adding 175,000 square feet in 2004.

The trend of creating unique themes was at its apex during the mid-1990's, as Las Vegas offered Egypt, Rome, New York and Monte Carlo to its visitors. And more was to come – Bellagio, Mandalay Bay, Paris, and the Venetian brought more exotic locales to Sin City, USA.

In 1996, Sheldon Adelson sold the world's largest and most popular technology trade show COMDEX for about $1 billion and announced his plans to build a new casino resort on the site of the

NEW YORK-NEW YORK

Sands Casino. The Venetian, opened with over 3,000 hotel rooms and created a suitable replica of a typical Venezia piazza. Its unique retail mall is constructed along an actual canal system (with real water), complete with singing gondoliers ferrying visitors around the retail mall.

The Paris casino boasts a replica of the Eiffel Tower and recreates a small café on a cobblestone street. By 1999, visitors to Las Vegas could have a brief taste of the world's most exotic cities, albeit a neon one with slot machines.

Over the years, Steve Wynn spoke about his vision of Las Vegas. At a time when Las Vegas was known for cheap food and few quality restaurants, he foretold of a city with culinary delights akin to New York City and Paris. Many people never believed the time would come when you could order fresh fish in the desert and have a meal worthy of worldwide recognition. But some of the world's greatest chefs have descended upon this oasis in

Fireworks at the Venetian

BELLAGIO GARDEN

the desert to build and operate some the most exciting restaurants ever created. With top chefs and restaurant operators from New York, Los Angeles, New Orleans, Paris, Rome, and almost every other food capital in the world, Las Vegas has truly become a haven for connoisseurs, people who make a great food an integral part of their lives. And the great part is that it is all in one city! Within just a few years, Steve Wynn saw his culinary vision become reality. Once again, he became the catalyst, luring the greatest chefs to his casino resorts. His vision reached its apex when he built the Bellagio and brought in some of the best restaurants to a single property.

Wynn continued his vision with the transformation of Las Vegas into an entertainment capital. Already thought to be the entertainment capital of the world, his vision was more refined than featuring recycled stars from yesteryear feeding their aging egos with shaky performances that verged on embarrassing. Wynn envisioned Broadway shows, top entertainers of today, and cultural offerings such as art galleries. Again acting as the catalyst, he opened an art gallery at the Bellagio and displayed many works from his impressive private collection. Las Vegas still has its share of recycled stars, but the hottest tickets are for top performers in the prime of their careers. Some show companies such as Cirque du Soleil have made Las Vegas a home, creating high-tech theatres customized for their performances.

CIRQUE DU SOLEIL "O" SHOW

The Design and Architecture of Today's Casino

Working with architects like Joel Bergman and Paul Steelman, Steve Wynn designed casino hotels with a three spoke design that had hotel rooms radiating out from the casino in the center. This design was almost required to service a hotel with over 3,000 rooms. The three-spoke or pinwheel became the design of choice, and was repeated for a number of casino resorts including Treasure Island, Bellagio, Venetian, Monte Carlo and others.

Volume, Volume, Volume

All of these things that Las Vegas has become, and is still becoming – mega-resorts (with convention space galore), food capital of the world, top entertainment, all contribute to one thing: Visitors. Las Vegas has been the second most visited city in the United States for many years, and is close to becoming number one. The city that holds the title of number one is Orlando, which had nearly 45 million visitors in 2003 – thanks to Disney World, of course. But with over 35 million people visiting much smaller Las Vegas in 2003, it is clearly a city challenged by the sheer volume of people.

INSIDE THE MIRAGE

The ability to manage the number of people visiting Las Vegas is possible only because of the technology employed every step of the way. From the airlines to the hotels to the shows, none of this would be possible without computer technology. It would be impossible to imagine 20,000 people descending upon the Flamingo on a single day in the 1950's – it just wouldn't be possible. In today's casino resorts, not only is it possible, but it happens almost every day.

From the six to eight thousand people that stay in the hotel, to the thousands more who visit the casino and the restaurants, only technology can make it all possible. And only good technology can make it a good experience for the customers and the employees. Gone are the days when the casino manager knew everyone by first name. First of all, there are too many casino managers working in one casino. Some casinos have over 100,000 square feet of gaming floor space, requiring multiple casino managers. And they could still never remember even a fraction of the millions of customers that visit each year. The only way to successfully manage interactions with the customer is with technology. Technology that helps identify, recognize, track, manage, and reward customers gives casino employees the ability to personalize their experience – and the better the systems, the better the experience.

Harrah's Entertainment
www.harrahs.com

The gaming industry has its share of high-profile entrepreneurial success stories, but the future belongs to great companies that, through technology, deliver the personal touch on a mass scale. In the 1990's and into the 21st Century, no casino operator invested more time, money, and organizational commitment to loyalty marketing than Harrah's Entertainment. As a result, Harrah's positioned itself as uniquely able to build lasting and profitable relationships with customers, the key to success in any mature industry environment.

Founded in 1937, Harrah´s Entertainment, Inc. is the world´s largest casino operator. Harrah's Entertainment owns or manages through various subsidiaries 27 casinos in the United States under the Harrah's, Horseshoe, Rio, Showboat and Harveys brand names. In the summer of 2004, Harrah's announced an agreement to acquire Caesars Entertainment, Inc.

The fully-merged company will include an enviable portfolio of Las Vegas megaresorts, adding Caesars Palace, Paris, Bally's and the Flamingo to Harrah's 13-state network of properties. Some 30 million Americans hold a Harrah's Total Rewards loyalty card, the program that is the linchpin of the company's success. Up to 20 million additional names could be merged with and added to Harrah's database when the Caesars acquisition is absorbed. This process would be overwhelming to any other casino operator, but not Harrah's, which in 2003 was recognized by *CIO Insight* magazine as the company that best aligned business strategy and information technology.

HARRAH'S ATLANTIC CITY

"Most companies only dream about understanding the customer," commented the judges. "Harrah's strategy established a vision for understanding the customer in entirely new ways."

Not bad for a company that started out as a humble bingo operation in Reno, where Bill Harrah, the company's founder, instilled many of the traits that sustain Harrah's Entertainment to this day. Harrah's focus on customer service and the details of the business was legendary, as was his ability to build a strong organization. In the 1940's, he asked for daily profit-and-loss statements for each department, a practice that was unheard of at the time. Whereas many casino owners lived in the count room to safeguard profits, Harrah delegated the task. His personal integrity and that of his company was unimpeachable, at a time when organized crime had infiltrated the industry. His management style was never autocratic, and his organization was always larger than others. He didn't insist on personal control, and he inspired a high degree of employee loyalty.

Harrah also appreciated the value of an outsider's eye in what was very much an insider's business. "Sometimes," he once said, "a newcomer can see a lot of things the old timers can't see." (1) A prophetic statement, given the unorthodox but visionary decision of Phil Satre, Harrah's Chairman, to turn the company over to a Harvard Business School professor named Gary Loveman in 2001.

Satre joined the company as General Counsel in 1978, the year of Bill Harrah's death, eventually rising to President and CEO and, in 1997, to Chairman of the company. He oversaw the company's entry into the Atlantic City market, riverboat gaming markets throughout the Midwest and the South, the negotiation of

Indian gaming management contracts from Arizona to California to North Carolina, and numerous acquisitions. Perhaps the most significant of Satre's innumerable contributions to Harrah's was his dogged insistence on a national loyalty marketing program and, working closely with IT executive John Boushy, the technological and operational changes needed to support it.

The logic behind a national loyalty marketing program was driven by internal and external considerations. Supported by a centralized database, a national loyalty program would make Harrah's the gaming industry's leading Customer Relationship Management (CRM) company. The strategy also had the benefit of being a logical way to differentiate Harrah's from the industry's other large, publicly-owned companies, which were driving traffic to their sites primarily by investing billions in new and expanded resorts. It was also a classic response to a maturing business environment, where the supply of a commodity product approaches demand. After all, from a customer's standpoint, a slot machine is a slot machine. With so many options for the player, why should they pledge more of their dollars to one casino brand over another?

Harrah's set out to tackle this problem by building an unsurpassed data-mining capability, one that would enable the company to predict the value of players, customize promotions and optimize revenue. The company would apply the same principles of successful loyalty programs in other industries. The frequent flyer gets more benefits at gold than at silver, and at platinum than at gold. They might even fly more just to retain, or maximize their status. Similarly, Harrah's would work to take an occasional player who patronizes many casinos and turn him into a loyal Harrah's customer.

HARRAH'S LAS VEGAS

The process began with building a centralized data system across multiple properties, which was not only expensive and time-consuming, it bumped against vested interests at the individual property level. Multiple systems gave way to uniformity whenever possible. Various ways of collecting information became one way of collecting information. Data gleaned from one property could be used to support the results of another property. The greater good was to prevail over personal preferences and agendas. The operational challenges of centralization were augmented by cultural challenges. Only a company with deeply-rooted organizational values could have pulled it off.

The first dividends came in 1994, when Harrah's, which had 8 properties, unified its systems under cc (Winner's Information Network), giving it the ability to share customer information across the entire organization. WINet combined the Harrah's transactional data systems, which capture information from the company's gaming, hotel, food-and-beverage and reservation systems, with its patron database, which holds all of the company's historical customer information.

"We built systems that pulled data from behind all the properties and added a push function that made the system perform more seamlessly as information went from one property to another or from one market to another," said Tim Stanley, senior vice president of information technology and chief information officer. "By having that data centrally, once we had a strong marketing team in place, it gave them the ability to think about the company and its customers differently and use data in a test-and-controlled kind of way. It was the overlaying of the data that helped us understand which things drive customer satisfaction, revenue and profitability. From that, came sophisticated marketing and changes in operational behavior. We moved from feudal fiefdoms of independent properties that happened to be linked under one name to running a company of stores."

The marketing team was assembled by Loveman, whom Satre had met at a seminar at the Harvard Graduate School of Business, where Loveman was a professor. Loveman, whose academic credentials include a Ph. D. in economics from MIT, recruited Rich Mirman, a Ph. D. candidate in mathematics at the University of Chicago who worked for Booz Allen & Hamilton management consulting, and David Norton, an expert direct mail marketer from American Express. This collection of outsider talent was unheard of in the gaming industry, and, combined with CIO Stanley, who heads a 550-employee IT department, they made Harrah's into a world-class marketing company.

Harrah's loyalty program debuted as Total Gold in 1997, was renamed Total Rewards in 1999 and TR2 (Total Rewards 2) in 2003. The payoffs were immediate. The number of individual customers visiting Harrah's casinos in multiple markets grew from 13 percent in 1997 to 23 percent in 1999, and Total Rewards helped the company double profits in the same time span. In 2000, Total Rewards was responsible for an increase of $165 million from top-tier players. By 2004, Harrah's reached the 30 million cardholder mark—a figure that represented between 33% to 40% of the target gaming population in the United States. From 1999 to 2004, Total Rewards helped Harrah's generate same-store sales growth in all but one of 24 financial quarters.

Harrah's Reno, Nevada

Of the 30 million participants in Total Rewards, just under 10 million are what Harrah's calls "frequent guests," which means they've visited at least once in the last 12 months. That group is grouped into tiers; gold, platinum, diamond or Seven Stars Club. Of frequent customers, between one-third to one-half share their e-mail address with Harrah's, and the ratio is higher with the company's best customers. The company concentrates on maximizing gaming revenue with its best customers. Everything, including technology, is mobilized in favor of this goal.

"Our yield management systems use a predictive value of a customer's gaming worth as well as room availability," explained Stanley. "Over 75% of our customers have tracked play, which means they use a Total Rewards card as part of their visit. For hotel customers, that figure is even higher. As a result, our yield management systems use a predictive value of a customer's gaming worth as well as room availability. From 2001 to 2003, depending on the market, we generated 15% to 20% increases in value per occupied room. So we're putting the right customers in the right room at the right time. You may not charge people at all for the room, which is counter-intuitive to what a lot of Vegas operators are doing."

None of this would have been possible without enormous investments in information technology and the development of organizational processes that helped make those investments sensible and profitable. Never content to rest on its laurels as the gaming industry IT leader, Harrah's maintained a relentless focus on systems integration, driving down the cost of computing, and managing its technology purchases the way a mutual fund would a portfolio. Depending on the level of investment, the firm developed processes by which the most expensive purchases are subject to the highest levels of scrutiny, including, at the top level of expenditure, timely assessments of project functionality, costs vs. benefits, deadlines and individual and departmental accountability.

Such discipline is indispensable; from 2001 to 2003, project throughput almost tripled, from 112 projects to 324 projects. By 2004, Harrah's was spending 2% of annual revenue on IT. That same year, it won *Baseline Magazine's* Technology ROI reward, registering an annual return on investment of 389%.

The vast majority of these investments have focused on the addition of CRM capabilities. In the early days there was a single touchpoint for card members: the Total Rewards center at a Harrah's property, where members would interact there via an employee. Harrah's then took the step of integrating all Total Rewards information into its call centers. When customers call 1-800-HARRAHS or interact with a property host on-site, all of their customer information is available to employees, allowing them to deliver memorable, personalized customer service to the guest. Harrah's was also an early adopter of kiosk technology in the late 90's, which enables players to swipe their card to see how many points they have, their available comps and then print out redeemable awards.

Another major project was the corporate website. "Today, the web has turned out to be a big channel for us," said Stanley. "Many people in the gaming industry look at the web as a branding and reservation vehicle. We go a lot further. Customers can access all of the direct mail and e-mail they've ever received from us, all the phone calls, and anything they've been offered. Much of this can be redeemed online."

For its casinos, Harrah's has architected and implemented what Stanley calls "iApps," an enterprise suite of integrated, interactive and intranet technology based applications that are developed and maintained centrally for use by all the Harrahs locations. These are web-based stations around the property where players swipe their card to enter a sweepstakes or promotion. The company has invested in a Player Contact System, which is a proactive tool that enables hosts to contact players with letters, phone calls and e-mails. When players are on-property, their hosts are alerted, allowing them to greet their customers as quickly as possible. "We've now got detailed analyticals, so that when you are on the property or shortly after you get home, you get surveyed," said Stanley. "All of that gets folded into the system."

Significant investments are continuously being made in integration. A wide range of systems are tied into Harrah's CRM database. Harrah's uses over 200 systems in all throughout its properties, but there are 15 to 20 systems that make up the heart of its CRM program. Whenever a customer interacts with a property (i.e., reserving a room, playing a particular slot machine or editing their membership profile), actionable information is the result. The key systems cover reservations, hotel property management, slot and table games, transactional systems such as point-of-sale machines and the Total Rewards website. Many of these systems are typically off-the-shelf products that don't talk to each other out of the box, a problem that Harrah's solved by purchasing middleware from Tibco, an initial investment Stanley described as, "breathtaking, but well worth the expense over time." Result: Whenever new data is generated, it is instantly published to all relevant CRM systems, updating customer profiles in real-time, a capability no other casino operator can match.

(1)Quoted in Robert L. Shook, Jackpot, (John Wiley & Sons, Inc. 2003), pg. 13.

Caesars Entertainment

www.caesars.com

In the history of the casino industry, no name has a higher profile than Caesars. But what's in a name when you boast the most impressive collection of brands in the business? Enormous marketing potential is one answer. Technological complexity is another. The Caesars portfolio includes the flagship property Caesars Palace, Bally's, Flamingo, Grand Casinos, Hilton and Paris. Markets served include Atlantic City, Las Vegas, Mississippi, Louisiana and Indiana. For all of that, each of Caesars' brand names had its own casino management system until 2002, a legacy of the growth-through-acquisition strategy that the company had pursued since 1996, when Hilton Hotel's casino group merged with Bally Entertainment. By 1999, the company, then known as Park Place Entertainment, had added Grand Casinos and Caesars World to the mix. Renamed Caesars Entertainment in 2004, the company had grown into one of the world's largest gaming operators, with $4.5 billion in annual net revenue at 28 properties on four continents. Along the way, management realized there was hidden gold in this collection of properties, but not so long as each had its own player card and loyalty marketing program. The solution was to develop a proprietary casino management system that would serve as the platform for a unified loyalty marketing program that would make Caesars an industry leader in Customer Relationship Management (CRM). Easier said than done, but Caesars had several things working in its favor. Chief among them was a strong management team, led by Wallace Barr, now President and CEO, a hands-on executive whose background was in operations. Barr's abiding philosophical commitment to customer loyalty and excellent personal relationships with property presidents transformed Caesars into a first-rate marketing company. "Barr's emphasis was to take a broader view of customer relationships," said Carol Pride, Chief Information Officer. "Our loyalty marketing, use of the Internet, campaign management and revenue management initiatives are all looked at from an enterprise perspective rather than an individual property per-

CEO AND PRESIDENT WALLACE R. BARR STANDS IN FRONT OF AN ARTIST'S RENDERING OF CAESARS WEMBLEY.

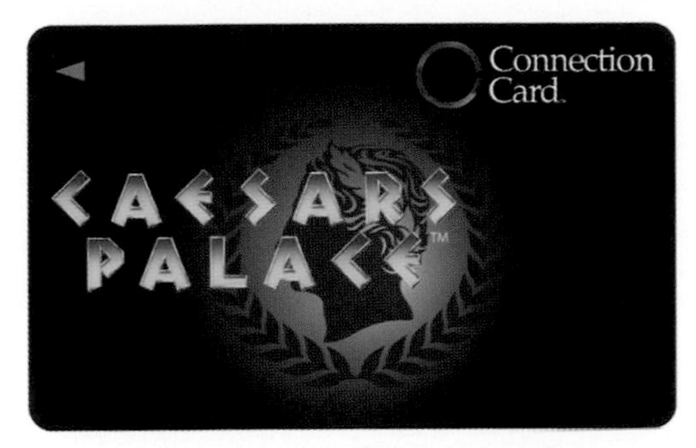

CAESARS PALACE CONNECTION CARD

spective." Pride's predecessor, Bob Conover, was another key player and an ex-IBM executive who had spent nearly 20 years with the company when the project began. Conover, now retired, was highly familiar with the strengths and limitations of Caesars' IBM AS/400 platform and fully conscious of the need to develop a system that had the flexibility to respond to a wide range of customer tastes and behaviors. The new system, which was fully implemented in 2002, linked all 18 U.S. properties with an advanced "ATM" (asynchronous transfer mode) communications network, a highly efficient solution that delivers scalable bandwidth to the desktop and transmits video, voice and data simultaneously. Information on Caesars' 26 million cardholders is piped to a regional-based data warehouse with a capacity of more than 6 trillion bytes. There it is sorted by a wide variety of metrics to give a comprehensive picture of customer behavior available for analysis in numerous systems. The system set the stage for the Connection Card, which enables customers to earn rewards at Caesars Entertainment resorts across the country. Other CRM initiatives were soon to follow. In 2003, Caesars became the first gaming operator to offer a company-wide comp rewards program based on total spending on hotels, dining, shopping, entertainment, as well as gaming, across all of its U.S. properties. That same year, it launched new websites for all its domestic casino resorts, resulting in a 54 percent increase in online room reservations over 2002. In 2004, Caesars' Web sites were ranked highest among gaming-hotel companies in treating online customers with respect. Caesars' next chapter promises to be even more dramatic. Its merger with Harrah's Entertainment, announced in 2004, will result in the consolidation of companies with a combined 57 million records in its database. Will the ultimate CRM company result? That is a possibility, given the strides that Caesars has made in a few short years, the organizational strengths it brings to the table, and the brands and properties at its disposal.

CAESARS PALACE, LAS VEGAS

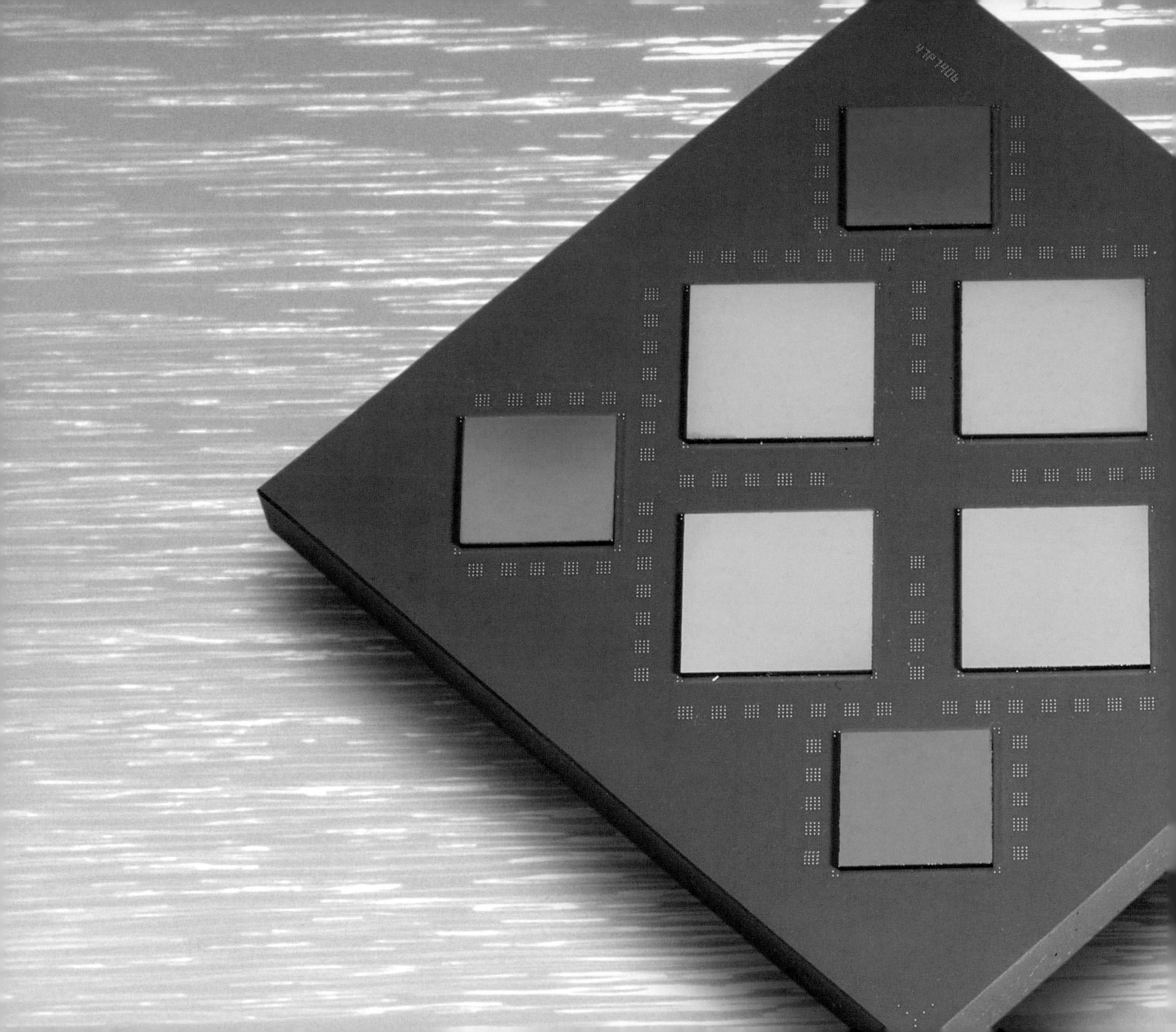

VI

The Evolution of Computer Systems in Casinos

In the Beginning

We know that casinos started with no computer systems at all, just accountants with sharp minds and sharp suits that counted all the money. As regulations were created and enforced, and as technology advanced to make computers available to businesses in the 1960's and 1970's, casinos started to use them like any other business. Most of these early computers were used for basic functions such as payroll, general ledger, and some basic human resources and marketing functions. There weren't many choices of software vendors during that time, and there weren't any options for casino related software – it all had to be custom written.

IBM Computers in Gaming

System/38

The IBM System/38 was a computer. It was a precursor to the AS/400 which was later called the iSeries. This was the brainchild of IBM engineer Frank Soltis.

Introduced following the System/34 and prior to the System/36, it was also a descendant of the fabled IBM 'FS' project, which was designed to be a followup/replacement for the System/360 and System/370.

System/38 and its descendants are unique in being the only existing commercial capability architecture computers. The earlier Plessey 250 was the only other computer with capability architecture ever sold commercially. Additionally, the System/38 and its descendants are the only commercial computers ever to use a machine interface architecture to isolate the application software and most of the operating system from hardware dependencies, including such details as address size and register size.

AS/400

The Application System/400 (AS/400) is an IBM minicomputer for general business and departmental use, introduced in 1988 and still in production under the names iSeries and i5. The AS/400 is an object oriented system with an integrated database that was designed to implement E.F.Codd's relational database model in the operating system and hardware. All software necessary to run this computer is included and integrated. More than 2,500 business software applications were available when the first AS/400 was delivered in 1988.

The AS/400 was the follow-on to the System/38 database machine, announced by IBM in 1978 and delivered in 1980. The first AS/400 systems (known by the development code names Silverlake and Olympic) were delivered in 1988, and the product line has been refreshed continually since then. IBM renamed the AS/400 to iSeries in 2000, as part of its e-Server branding intiative. The product line was further extended in 2004 with the introduction of the i5 servers, the first to utilize the IBM POWER5 processor. The AS/400 was the first general purpose computer system to attain a C2 security rating from the NSA, and in 1995 was first to employ a 64-bit processor and operating system. The architecture of the system allows for future implementation of 128-bit processors when they become available. Existing programs will utilize the new hardware without modification.

The machine was originally based on a custom IBM CISC CPU which used an architecture known as Internal MicroProgrammed Interface (IMPI). It was later migrated to a PowerPC based RISC CPU family eventually known as RS64. The latest models are based on the POWER5 (announced 4 May 2004) processor.

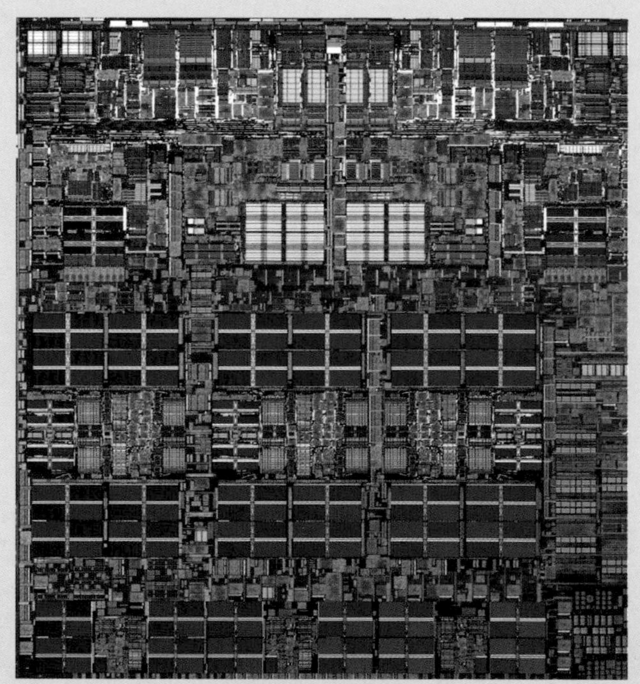

POWER5 Chip Die

The machine survives because the hardware abstraction layer of its microcode (called TIMI for "Technology Independent Machine Interface" by IBM) allows the operating system and application programs to take advantage of advances in hardware and software without recompilation. This means that a program written and compiled on an S/38 can be run as a native 64 bit program. The HAL allows a system that costs $9000 to run the exact same operating system and software as a $2 million system. The system can concurrently run multiple operating systems (i5/OS (OS/400), Linux, AIX) natively, and runs Windows Server on one or more blade servers when installed. The 64-bit design provides for the seamless addressing of up to 16 exabytes (16 million terabytes) of storage.

It was designed as the successor of the IBM System/38 and the IBM System/36. The programmers that worked on OS/400, the operating system of the AS/400, did not have a UNIX background. Dr. Frank Soltis, the head architect, says that this is the main difference between this and any other operating system.

Despite the lack of "UNIX-Y" background, the AS/400 has over the years, picked up the programming/runtime model found on UNIX, Linux, and PC systems. Traditional AS/400 programming is a "one-stop shop," where a programmer writes computer code, compiles the code, and then executes the code. There is no link step that is found in other environments.

RS/6000

The IBM pSeries, formerly called RS/6000 (for RISC System/6000), is IBM's current RISC/UNIX-based workstation computer line. Announced in 1990, the RS/6000 replaced the RT-PC. It is based on the IBM POWER CPU architecture and runs the AIX operating system.

IBM began delivery of RS/6000 products in February of 1990 [1,2]. IBM developed these products in response to customer needs for workstations and midrange systems with UNIX operating systems. The processors in these products were implementations of the POWER Architecture, a second generation reduced instruction set computer (RISC) architecture.

The POWER Architecture diverged somewhat from the path taken by most other RISC architectures. The primary objective of those architectures was to be sufficiently simple so that implementations could have a very short cycle time, which would result in processors that could execute instructions at the fastest possible clock rate. The designers of the POWER Architecture chose to minimize the total time required to complete a task. The total time is the product of three components: path length, number of cycles needed to complete an instruction, and cycle time.

Digital Equipment

PDP-11

The PDP-11 was a 16-bit minicomputer sold by Digital Equipment Corp. in the 1970s and 1980s. The PDP-11 was a successor to DEC's PDP-8 computer in the PDP series of computers. It had several uniquely innovative features, and was easier to program because a programmer could memorize the operations and the methods of accessing operands. They could then predict that any access method (or "addressing mode") would work with any operation; they did not have to learn a list of exceptions or special cases in which an operation had a special or restricted set of addressing modes.

In the most radical departure from other, earlier computers, the PDP-11 had no dedicated bus for input/output; it had only a memory bus. All input and output devices were mapped to addresses in memory, so in addition, no special I/O instructions were needed. The interrupt system was intentionally designed to be as simple as possible, while assuring that no event in an interrupt sequence could be missed.

Source: Wikipedia

At the time many casinos started using computers, Microsoft was just burgeoning into a real company and IBM had captured much of the market. In fact, in the early days, IBM had basically the entire casino market. Their presence was mostly computers and operating software – many of the applications were custom programmed because there wasn't enough market demand to create off-the-shelf packages for the casinos.

Traditional operating departments such as payroll, finance, and human resources were usually handled by software packages that were used in other industries. But the casino needed custom applications for casino management, credit, cage, marketing, slots, and tables. These custom applications grew as the industry grew, often spawning small companies dedicated to developing and supporting applications for the gaming industry.

One of the very first casino systems created by Bally Systems was a slot accounting system installed in nearly every casino in America. Bob Conover, formerly of IBM and later the Vice President of Information systems for Bally's Casino in Atlantic City, helped to create one of the most successful gaming system companies. Over the years, Bally Systems has competed with a number of start-ups, large and small, including, CDS, IGT, and Acres. The fact that the Bally System is still installed in a large number of casinos is a testament to the stability and success of the system. As CIO of Caesars Entertainment for over twenty years, one could argue that Bob Conover has quietly had a very profound impact on technology in the gaming industry. Even as Conover prepares to take on new challenges, his impact will be felt for years to come.

The Sands Casino Hotel in Atlantic City launched two casino software systems that became ubiquitous in casinos throughout the country. The first was Logical Solutions Incorporated, LSI, headed by Russ Keil. The second was Advanced Casino Systems Corporation, ACSC, formed by Larry Cole in 1997. Recently, ACSC was purchased by Alliance Gaming, the parent company of Bally Gaming and Bally Systems.

These systems, as well as the many others that have been developed in similar fashion over the last twenty years, all run on IBM computer platforms. LSI provided the casino management applications while ACSC and Bally Systems provided the slot accounting and slot player tracking applications. LSI, while no longer operating, is still installed in many casinos around the country! Some of the software programs can still be found running in Atlantic City. ACSC has grown over the years to be a complete solution for slots, tables, casino management, and marketing. The purchase of ACSC by Alliance has given the company much needed resources, but since it is now one of two slot solutions offered by Bally, it raises questions about the permanence of the ASCS solution.

RIGHT: CAESARS, 1986

As advances in technology have helped PC's and server solutions explode over the last five to ten years, Microsoft and its supporting cast of vendor companies such as Cisco and Sun, have increased their presence in gaming and every other industry. When IBM computers were installed in casinos in the early 1980's, there weren't many gaming applications for the platform. But that has changed over the last five years, as there are more and more applications being developed for server-based platforms running Microsoft operating systems.

One of the few early competitors to the IBM and SDS casino kingdom was a company called EDT. EDT was a completely PC-based slot accounting and slot player tracking system that enjoyed some early success and then joined the IGT brand. Only a company the size of IGT could develop, sell, and support a PC-based slot system to compete with the IBM platform. Over the years, the IGT Smart System was able to develop better user interfaces and provide more bells and whistles which helped them win much of the new casino business that was fueled by the gaming industry explosion.

Computers and Casinos Along the Boardwalk and Beach

When the Golden Nugget opened in Atlantic City in 1980, it had some of the most reliable computers ever built—Tandems. Tandem computers were used for the most critical business applications, like banking transactions and stock trades on Wall Street. The Dow Jones even used Tandem computers because of their unique approach to fault tolerance – built-in redundancy. The Tandem Non-Stop computers were just that – non-stop. Every component of the system had a back-up: the processors, the disk drive storage, even the connections to the disk drives were redundant. That way, if any component ever failed, the back-up would take over instantly, providing no down time for the users. Casino executives were sold on the idea of never having to delay issuing credit or comps to a customer.

Tandem Computers was founded in 1974 by a group of engineers from Hewlett-Packard, led by James Treybig. Their business plan called for systems that were proof from "single point failures" and only slightly more expensive than competing non-fault tolerant systems. Tandem considered this to be very important to their business model, as customers

JAMES TREYBIG,
CO-FOUNDER TANDEM COMPUTERS

TANDEM COMPUTERS

Design of their NonStop I system was complete in 1975, and the first example was sold to Citibank in 1976. The NonStop I ran a custom operating system called Guardian that was key to the system's failover modes. A number of other companies had introduced failover that operated by restarting programs on other CPU's, but in Guardian all operations used message passing and were checkpointed for every operation. That is, Guardian could restart from any instruction in the program, a key feature that the stack-based processor made fairly easy to construct because it had little "state" to move from machine to machine. All instructions consisted of taking data from the stack and putting it back on when it completed, and if the latter failed the stack could be copied to another processor and restarted at that instruction.

While conventional systems of the era, including mainframes, had failure rates on the order of a few days, the NonStop system was designed to fail 100 times less, with "uptimes" measured in years. Nevertheless the NonStop was deliberately designed to be price-competitive with conventional systems, with a simple 2-CPU system priced at just over two times that of a competing single-processor mainframe, as opposed to four or more times of most competing solutions.

NonStop I was followed by the NonStop II in 1981, a slight improvement in speed to 0.8 MIPS, but a more measurable upgrade in memory from a maximum of 384kB per CPU in the I, to 2MB in the II, and the addition of a complete virtual memory system allowing for considerably larger address spaces. In 1986 a major upgrade to the system was introduced, the NonStop VLX. VLX used a new Dynabus, increasing speed from 13MBps to 40MBps (total, 20MBps per independent bus). VLX was partnered with the NonStop CLX, a minicomputer sized machine for smaller installations.

The NonStop Cyclone was introduced in 1989, introducing a new superscalar CPU design. It was otherwise similar to earlier systems, although much faster. In general terms the Cyclone was about four times as fast as the CLX 800, which Tandem used as their benchmark.

Tandem was acquired by Compaq in 1997. In an ironic full-circle, Compaq was later acquired by HP in 2002, bringing Tandem back to its original roots. As of 2003, the NonStop product line continues to be produced, under the HP name.

Source: Wikipedia

invariably developed procedural solutions to downtime when the price was too high. Source: Wikipedia

But casinos using the Tandem computers had a different problem. While the non-stop concept was great in that there would never be any interruption in service to the customers, there was no casino software written for Tandem computers. And because the operating system was quite different from anything that IBM used, the programs that were running in other casinos were not compatible with the Tandem. At that time Steve Wynn was the only casino owner using the Tandem computers in his Golden Nugget Casinos in Las Vegas and Atlantic City.

Tandem computers were quite different from IBM and other computers in that they were one of the first to use "client/server" architecture. The server portion of the program would service multiple clients and do the heavy-lifting of reading and writing to the database.

IBM PC INTRODUCED IN 1981

The clients were replicated on each terminal and did the work of displaying and accepting data on the screens. This architecture was very efficient, but because it was different from traditional computers, it required uniquely trained programmers.

Wynn's executive team always operated under the premise of *get it done or get a new job*, so they were very motivated to find solutions to all sorts of challenges. They hired some independent programmers that were very familiar with the Tandem, but not casinos, to write all the gaming systems for the Tandem computers. Working closely with Golden Nugget casino executives, they quickly became casino experts themselves, developing software that would help manage the casino and its customers.

The software they wrote was great because it was customized to the way the casinos conducted their business. The Tandem computers were for the most part non-stop, but there certainly were times when the computers were not available. System upgrades were most often the culprit, but if you made enough mistakes with the Tandem computers, you could get them to crash.

A common occurrence in the gaming industry is "casino hopping," when employees work for a short time at one casino, then go to work for another casino for a better paying job—or because they were fired at the last casino. Because their experience is unique and therefore valuable, they can usually find another job just down the street in short order. Such was the case with some of the IT employees in Atlantic City. Some of them brought the experience of working with Tandem computers to the Playboy Casino and the Showboat in Atlantic City and convinced the casino owners to follow the lead of Steve Wynn and install the highly reliable Tandem NonStop computers. As one might suppose, the software developed for Steve Wynn was proprietary and not available at your neighborhood software store. This required these casinos to also custom develop their own software on the Tandems. And like any smart business operator, they hired the programmers that had experience writing casino software.

As the Tandem computers and contract programmers made their way from one end of the boardwalk to the other, they deposited their casino systems, each with more customizations. While the systems they developed for Playboy and Showboat were different from each other, they still contained remnants of the original systems --- which was understandable, since the same programmers wrote all the systems. One rumor supported by many people was that some reports printed at Playboy and Showboat actually had "Golden Nugget" printed at the top of each page! It wouldn't be that surprising – and would have been fixed immediately. If the New Jersey Casino Control Commission (NJ CCC) or New Jersey Division of Gaming Enforcement (NJ DGE) ever saw a report like that, there surely would have been an investigation and possible fines levied against the casinos.

EARLY NONSTOP FAULT TOLERANT COMPUTER SYSTEM

Technology Advances

Some of the engineers that helped design and build the original PC-based slot system for IGT left and started their own company. John Acres created Acres Gaming, one of the more successful companies. After starting slowly and then hurdling a few bumps in the road, Acres soon had a product that was the envy of the other software companies. Also running on a PC-based platform, the Acres system provided the slot accounting and slot player tracking functions, but utilized the latest technology advancements to maximize user features. The bonusing features of the Acres System were also a key to its success, helping to generate significant additional revenues at the slot machines. After some time and a number of lawsuits, IGT decided they could not compete with Acres, so they bought the company in 2003!

As technology developed and distributed by Microsoft makes it easier and faster to design and develop on the PC platform, they continue to gain market share on IBM. But IBM is no slouch and is also creating tools to enhance development on their platforms. The deciding factor today seems to be the preference of the CIO; some are "true blue" and will stack their IBM iSeries against anything Microsoft has to offer. Others have adopted the Microsoft culture and see the advantages to lower maintenance costs, faster development, and portability. To be sure, the Internet will also help swing companies over to the Microsoft camp as more and more solutions become subscription-based. With no real winner in sight, the battle will wage on with the benefit going to the gaming companies. As in any competition, the result will be better products and better prices.

LEFT: IBM i520 AND i570

The Basics

Slot systems track two basic types of data: accounting data and customer data for each slot machine on the casino floor. In addition to that, they also support marketing activities and operational support for the slot department. To what degree they accomplish this is arguable, especially among casino operators.

There are quite a number of vendors offering slot system solutions, but the companies that enjoy the largest installation base are Bally, IGT, and Aristocrat. A couple of years ago, Acres and ACSC would also have been on that list, but they have been acquired by IGT and Bally, respectively.

In their fundamental mission of data collection, these systems are all fairly accurate, considering the task at hand. Tracking accounting data requires logging every coin-in, coin-out, jackpot, hopper fill, bonus, comp, bill validator, etc., and of course, all the meters. It took years, but the vendors worked to get their systems as accurate as possible, reducing or sometimes eliminating manual meter-reads.

Now the slot manufacturers (ironically, the owners of the slot systems) have thrown a wrinkle at the slot systems: ticket-in and ticket-out. The advent and increasingly rapid expansion of ticket-in/ticket-out slot machines, along with machine-played bonuses, has helped reduce operating costs and increase revenues for casinos. However, many of the slot systems are struggling to keep pace with these innovations. Beyond the issue of standardization, which is a major point of contention for manufacturers, vendors, and operators, the sheer volume of transactions can be overwhelming. In some cases, it has indeed overwhelmed the systems, causing them to crash. Imagine having your slot system down on a Saturday night – well, it has happened to some casinos already, and you can bet it will likely happen again.

Some of the problems are scary. In 2004, there was one incident at a major casino hotel in which the ticket redemption machine was timing-out on some transactions. The ticket was returned and the customers were instructed to see a cage cashier for their money. The problem arose when the next customer used the redemption machine – it would pay out the amount due the previous customer from the transaction that had timed-out! Think of the chaos—the accounting issues and customer service impact – not to mention the money lost. The source of the problem was identified in the slot system, related to ticket-in/ticket-out.

The problem, of course, is that these slot systems were not designed with many of these innovations in mind, resulting in a game of catch-up. The machine side of the slot company develops a new technological advance that is attractive to casino operators and profitable for the slot company. The system side of the slot company modifies the slot system to accommodate the new technology, such as ticket-in/ticket-out. There is always pressure to finish the modifications as quickly as possible. Then they have to roll out the solution to all of their customers.

Data Collection or Information System

Most of the slot systems offer, or claim to offer, tools for marketing and slot operations. And actually, some of them do a good job of providing basic functionality for direct marketing and slot analysis. Yet the vast majority of casino operators supplement these features with secondary systems or even outsourcing, reducing the role of the slot system to a mere data collection device. Casino operators are increasingly utilizing ERP systems that allow integration of multiple data sources such as casino, hotel, retail, and food & beverage. While this makes sense from a strategic marketing perspective, it is still the slot system that is used to support the execution of these strategies. Specifically, when customers are on-property, it is the slot system that is used to identify, locate, service, and support the customers. Therefore, it must continue to evolve as an information system, not just a data collection device. Moreover, casino operators must learn how to use these systems in their intended role and not rely solely on a massive marketing solution that may not have up-to-the-minute information.

Linking Customer Databases from Multiple Properties Together

Gaming companies realized that the fastest way to significantly increase their revenues was to buy another casino. It was faster than building a new casino, and usually much easier. They also realized that in order to have access to the cash they needed to acquire these casinos, their stock would need to be publicly traded on the stock market. So, following the original lead of Howard Hughes and soon thereafter Bill Harrah, the gaming companies of Kirk Kerkorian, Arthur Goldberg, and Steve Wynn went public. As if this weren't profitable enough for the casinos, they continued to expand their existing properties, extend their offerings into new jurisdictions, and merge and acquire other gaming companies.

As the merger game continues to be played out in the gaming industry at a frenzied pace, casino companies added properties to their portfolio creating opportunities for efficiency in purchasing, marketing, and technology. Some moved faster than others, and most ignored the possibility of combining customer databases – except Harrah's Entertainment. Phil Satre, CEO at the time of the explosive growth in the 1990's, realized immediately the potential. Most casinos required a customer to join a player club at each casino they owned, even if they were across the street from each other. Harrah's introduced one card that allowed players to accumulate points regardless of the Harrah's property they played in, and appropriately allow them to redeem their rewards at any Harrah's location. The program, originally launched in 1997 as Total

Gold, was renamed Total Rewards in 1999. According to press releases, Harrah's doubled their profits in the first two years of launching this program. But other gaming companies were slow to jump on the "one card" band wagon, which surely worked to Harrah's advantage.

The reasons for having one card that worked in multiple properties were obvious to Harrah's:

- **Resources of Entire Corporation Available (Dollars, People, Ideas, Properties):** Instead of each property marketing individually and potentially competing with other properties in the same corporation, financial and human resources can be combined allowing a stronger, more dominant marketing campaign that allows marketing at a national level. This allows the capture of a larger market share within the same jurisdiction and in

RIGHT: BILL HARRAH WITH BILL COSBY

other geographic regions. It also reduces costs, eliminates mailing redundancy, and perhaps most importantly, provides a distinct competitive advantage.

• **Build Brand Loyalty to Corporation:** Customers are enticed to visit the same brand property in all jurisdictions. Think about how often a person chooses a particular airline or hotel in order to earn points or miles in their favorite program.

• **Integration of Data:** This makes more information available to better understand which marketing campaigns, customer service, and other programs and systems work, and which ones do not work. Integrating data from multiple properties paints a more complete picture of a customer's profile.

• **Technology Upgrade:** It provides an opportunity to migrate from legacy systems to newer technology. Newer hardware and software upgrades enhance system features and are an attractive benefit of this concept. Most importantly, it helps to get all properties on the same software - and the same version of the software.

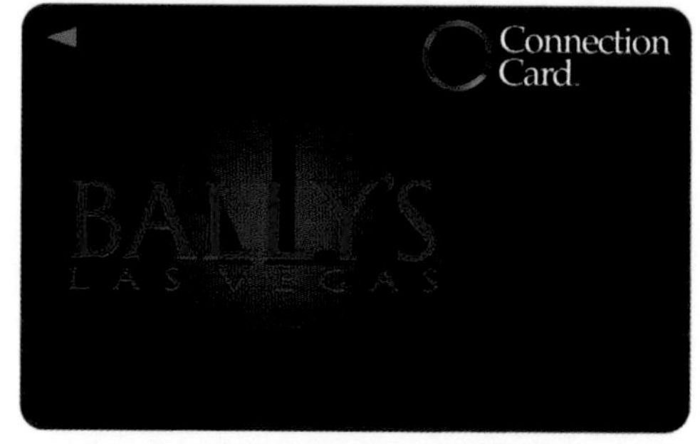

BALLY'S CONNECTION CARD

Although the technology existed to effectively implement this one card program, it was not an inexpensive proposition. But the biggest challenge wasn't the technology or even the money for the effort. It was the business model. At the time, presidents and general managers of casino properties were evaluated and rewarded based on the performance of their individual casino hotel. Understandably, they were reluctant to offer complimentaries and cash to customers that played at a sister property. The accounting was easy to work out by assigning the cost back to the original property based on the percentage of play at that casino. The challenge was twofold: convincing the management of the property to buy-in to the concept and support the implementation; and having the corporation successfully implement the program.

After working out the difficult challenge of changing the business model of how individual casino properties and their general managers were evaluated, the technological challenges still remained. Some of these technology issues were quite formidable and required large projects, extensive resources, and considerable budgets. Some of the technology challenges included:

• **Same Company, Different Platforms in Different Locations:** Some corporations had casinos running completely different software applications on different technology.

• **Same Company, Same Platforms, Different Applications or Versions in Different Locations:** Many properties may have had the same technology but had different applications installed or different versions of the same software at different casinos.

- **Data Relationships (Type, Frequency, Trip Definition, Summary Levels, Etc.):** This was probably one of the most challenging IT issues. There may have been a significant conversion required if all the properties were not using the same definitions. For example, if a casino property in Atlantic City defines a trip as a day (a 24 hour period) and the Las Vegas property defines it as no activity in a 72 hour period, trip activity will not be accurate until the data is converted or archived.
- **Customer Databases (Redundancy, Sensitivity, Varying Historical Data, Etc.):** In addition to the data definitions, there was the issue of the customer database itself. The cleansing of the database and combination of historical data requires major data conversions, cleansing and merging of customer accounts.
- **Card Readers:** It was very possible that when new systems were installed, the card readers on the slot machines would have to be replaced. This was a very expensive requirement, resulting in additional costs of millions of dollars.
- **Real Time Versus Batch Updates:** A decision also needed to be made regarding when the data would be rolled up to the central database (or distributed to each location). For corporations with properties in different geographic locations, batch would probably work fine because it was unlikely that players would travel and play the same day. However, for corporations with more than one property in the same town (e.g., Las Vegas) it was very likely that customers would visit multiple sites in one day, which would require a real time update.
- **Comp Cost Considerations:** Finally, the cost of complimentaries must be consistent for all properties or a complicated database would be required to maintain the associated costs for each type of comp at each property. For example, the room cost in Las Vegas is very different from Atlantic City.

While the challenges may have seemed insurmountable, Harrah's pressed forward with their Total Reward program and their efforts paid off. Harrah's now boasts over 30 million customers in their database, and when the acquisition of Caesars Entertainment was completed in 2005, it topped 50 million.

Within just a few years of Harrah's completing their one card program, other gaming corporations such as MGM Mirage, Station Casinos, Caesars Entertainment, and Isle of Capri launched their own one card programs and enjoyed similar success. Although Harrah's no longer has the exclusive program in the industry, they still arguably have the best, with a continued focus on improving the technology and delivery to the customer.

InfoGenesis

www.infogenesis.com

A leading provider of information technology for the hospitality and food service industries, InfoGenesis develops software that can dramatically increase the customer experience as well as enhance the business process, including point-of-sale (POS), reservation management, dining management, and business intelligence. The company also provides hardware, installation, training, consulting, and award-winning customer support for a complete, feature-rich solution.

Based in Santa Barbara, Calif., and headed by President and CEO Terry Cunningham, InfoGenesis products and services are designed expressly to personalize and enhance the customer experience in a variety of venues, including casinos, table-service restaurants, chain hotels and resorts, cruise ships, and institutional food-service operations. The company offers back-office management tools for stand-alone properties and multi-site enterprises as well as flexible front-of-the-house touch screen, kiosk, and portable wireless solutions.

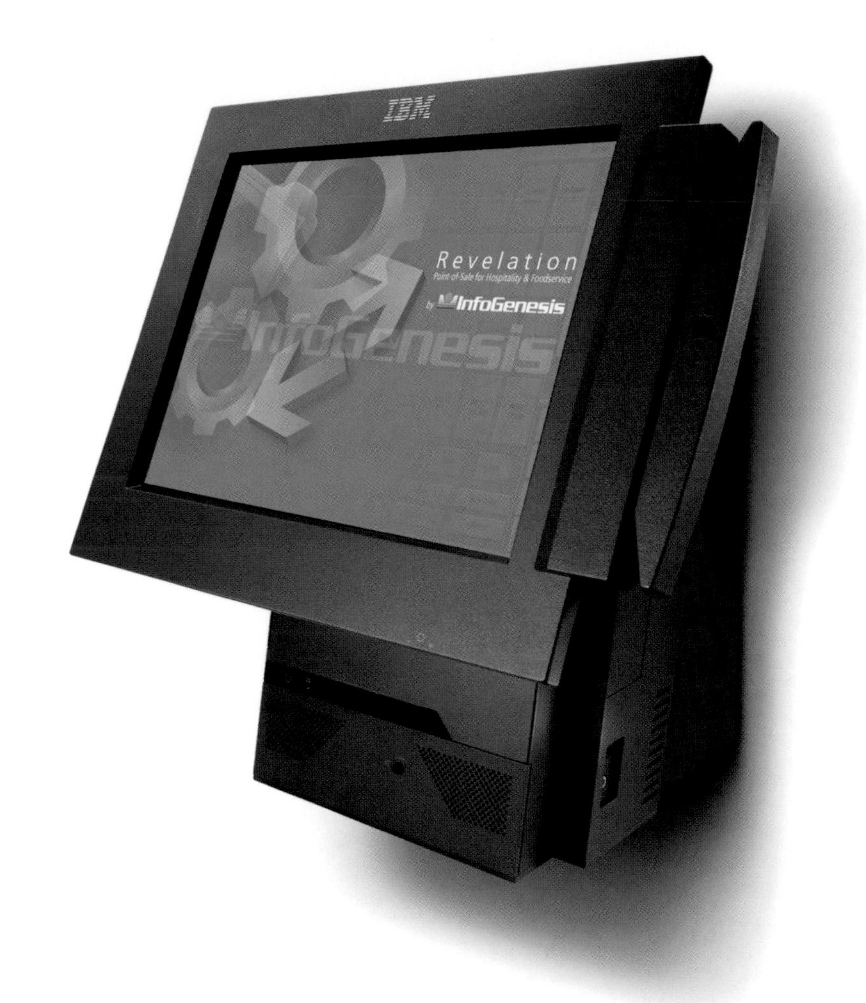

INFOGENESIS REVELATION

To serve their customers, InfoGenesis provides innovative software for gaining an integrated, enterprise-wide business picture. In multi-million-dollar casinos such as the Morongo Casino Resort & Spa and Mandalay Bay Resort & Casino, the company's products help run more efficient, more cost-effective, and more revenue-producing operations throughout the resorts' entertainment, lodging, restaurant, and retail services areas.

Using advanced Microsoft technology, IBM servers, and IBM SurePOS point-of-sale touch screen terminals, InfoGenesis products make managing operations and collecting and analyzing customer data much easier. The company does everything from enabling cashless payment options such as e-payment to controlling inventory to reducing shrinkage to providing mobile POS options to improving event and food service management. By using InfoGenesis technology, some customers have seen a 15% increase in revenues as well as much greater customer satisfaction.

Two core InfoGenesis products, Revelation and Rendezvous, provide extensive capabilities and features. Revelation is flexible software that provides access to data from all levels of a hospitality, food service, or retail operation in real-time. By gathering this information and making it easily accessible, Revelation helps management leverage unit-level details across the enterprise and identify opportunities for significant return on investment.

Rendezvous is a customizable enterprise-wide reservation and dining-management system that lets users book reservations for any of their properties—restaurants, hotels, spas, or casinos—whether a few blocks away or in a far corner of the globe. In addition to providing central booking, the solution helps management coordinate customer service efforts and provides important data on who customers are and what they want. This in turn helps operators offer superior guest service.

Both Revelation and Rendezvous are award-winning products. In 2003 each was chosen as one of the *Top Twenty Most Innovative Gaming Products* by the American Gaming, Lodging, and Leisure Summit. In 2004 both products were named one of the *Top Twenty Most Innovative New Gaming Products* by the Casino Journal.

In addition to providing venue operators with

Handheld Order Processing Unit

superior information technology, InfoGenesis offers Web-based product training and other professional business services. The training, called InfoGenesis Connect, lets owners train their staff cost-effectively and on their own schedule and site. Classes with multimedia features are accessed through the Internet and address users at all levels.

InfoGenesis Professional Business Services helps hospitality and food-service providers meet their business needs and improve personal customer touches. Analysts review and evaluate the information gathered by Revelation to gain increased insight into available opportunities, ways to streamline operations, and how to ensure the best possible customer experience. Custom reports and business reviews are some of the services offered.

Point-of-sale and business intelligence information is key to running a successful casino operation. Not only does it enable management to run an efficient, effective business, but it also provides information about customers' behaviors, showing providers how to reach them and make their marketing approaches more effective. By offering reliable, cutting-edge customer experience management technology, InfoGenesis is helping to make gaming a profitable growth industry.

FINAL BIOS
02-03-03
CHTL
D F Rev. 5.1
Actel
A54SX32
P0208
0322
A-008318-06
PCBA, CPU-I/O
Copyright 2002
WMS
GAMING

VII

Technology in Today's Casino

WMS Circuit Board

The progression of technology in today's casinos is nothing short of amazing. In just a few decades, casinos went from having just a few accounting systems to having a computer application for almost anything that can be automated. A favorite trivia question for casino operators is to ask someone how many different computer systems they think the casino uses. The responses vary from a few to as many as twenty, thirty or even sometimes as high as fifty. The casino operators always enjoy telling them the real answer: over 200! That certainly is at the high end of the spectrum, as most casino hotels have more like 125 - 150 different computer systems. While it's easy for people to imagine the typical systems such as hotel, finance, human and casino management, they are often hard pressed to think of some of the more obscure systems such as the uniform management system or the two valet parking systems. Casinos need one system to track the car, and another to take pictures of the car from all angles for insurance purposes.

Here are some of the systems that are used by casinos today, grouped by function or area:

CASINO
- Casino Management
- Slot Accounting
- Credit Application Processing
- Credit Management
- Signature Verification
- Check Cashing
- Credit Card Advance
- Pit/Table Player Tracking
- Keno
- Bingo
- Casino Reservations
- Key Management
- Direct Marketing
- Event Management
- Ticket Management
- Slot Player Tracking
- Card Shufflers
- Progressive System
- Slot Maintenance Tracking
- Slot Key Management
- Slot Tournament System
- Customer Management/Host System
- Complimentary Issuance
- Dealer Scheduling

HOTEL
- Property Management System (PMS)
- Concierge System
- Room Key Management
- Valet Parking Ticket Management
- Valet Parking Car Picture
- In-Room Movies/Cable TV
- High-Speed Internet Access
- Coat Check
- Luggage Check
- Hotel Kiosks
- Closed-Circuit TV Advertising
- Hotel Yield Management
- Hotel Reservations
- In-Room Safes
- Spa Reservations/Management
- Housekeeping Dispatch
- Engineering (HVAC Management)
- Engineering Maintenance Tracking
- Call Accounting

FOOD & BEVERAGE/RETAIL
- Point-of-Sale System
- Liquor Control
- Catering System
- Convention Space Management System
- Menu Costing
- Inventory System
- Restaurant Seating

COMMUNICATIONS
- PBX System
- Employee Radios
- Music and Paging System

HUMAN RESOURCES AND FINANCE
- Human Resources System
- Time and Attendance
- Applicant Tracking
- Finance (General Ledger/Account Receivable/Accounts Payable)
- Badging System
- Purchasing/Inventory System
- Credit Card Processing
- Wardrobe/Dry Cleaning
- Uniform Management System
- Job Ticketing
- Labor Management System
- Risk Management
- Payroll
- Scheduling
- Training
- License Management
- Employee Cash Advance ATM's
- Customer ATM's

SURVEILLANCE/SECURITY
- Casino Surveillance
- Non-Casino Surveillance
- Security System
- Restricted List Management
- Government Security Systems

ENTERTAINMENT
- Stage Lighting
- Lounge Lighting
- Event Center Lighting
- Ticketing
- Sound System

INFORMATION TECHNOLOGY
- Company Website
- Company Intranet
- Company Email
- PC Operating Systems
- PC Suite of Applications
- Optical Data Storage
- Uninterrupted Power Supply (UPS) System
- Door Access Keypad Management
- Enterprise Data Management
- Data Warehouse
- PC Network

This is a representative sample, but does not account for systems that are duplicated for multiple departments, nor does it take into account the myriad of spreadsheets that are created from data extracted from these systems. One of the most important reports created each day for casino executives is the Daily Operating Report or DOR. This report, contained in just one or two pages, is a summary of all revenue and activity from the previous day and usually compares it to the same day the previous year. Because it requires data from many of the systems installed in the casino resort, and then requires some fancy formatting, it is usually created manually each day by a financial analyst. Some casinos can actually produce much of the data from one report that draws data from the appropriate systems, but there is always some information that is not available and must be added manually, such as the weather, group events, or the number of people served in the buffet.

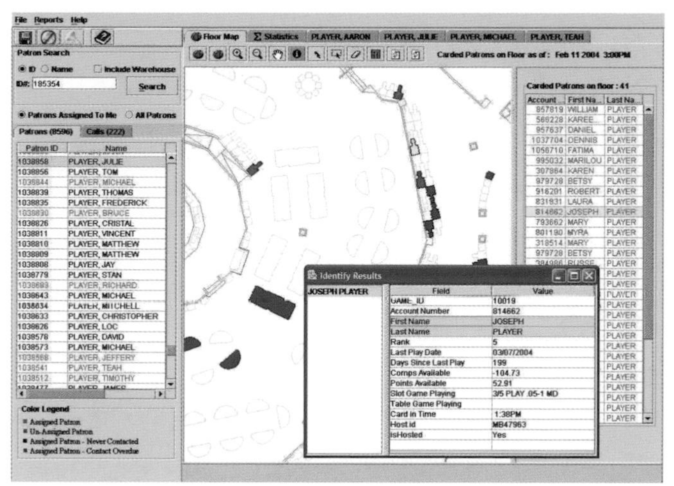

PCS Screen Shot

The technology of the modern casino is very complex, requiring careful management and strong IT leadership to be successful. Among the many challenges that IT leaders face in their day-to-day lives is the integration of mission critical systems to provide employees with information, not just data. Computer systems in casino resorts are used for a variety of reasons including safeguarding customers and employees, protecting the assets of the company, and increasing shareholder wealth.

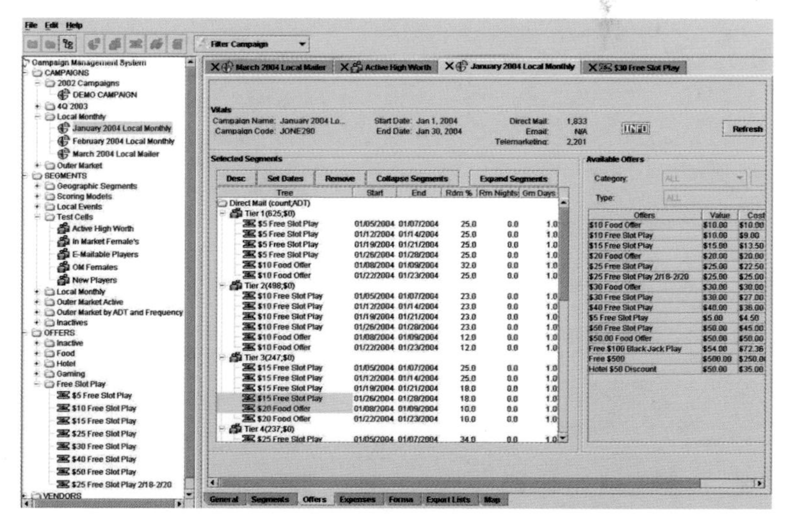

CMS Screen Shot

The first priority of any company is always to safeguard customers and employees from harm. This is accomplished by using a combination of cameras, door locks, computer systems, and security personnel, along with a set of approved procedures and regulations imposed by governing bodies such as the Gaming Commission and state and federal laws. This covers everything from people trying to rob the casino to employees pilfering casino chips to organized crime laundering money.

The systems, procedures, and training in place at the casinos are designed specifically to protect the customers and employees, and are updated frequently to keep pace with the attempts of nefarious individuals that would seek to circumvent the safeguards.

After the protection of the customers, employees, and assets of the casino are addressed, the technology is focused on the management of the casino. This includes controlling costs and increasing revenues. All computer systems that are used for managing the casino help to control costs by creating an efficient operation and reducing labor where possible. Sophisticated computer systems are used to schedule employees and dealers to maximize efficiency, to purchase food and supplies to save money, and to track and store data to reduce labor.

The computer systems that are used for generating revenues are usually dedicated to the marketing efforts of the casino hotel. The lifeblood of most casinos is direct marketing. More than any other marketing tool, it is the most effective means to increase revenue at the casino. Casinos collect data about their customers and track their activity in great detail in order to craft marketing offers that will bring those customers back to the casino for another trip. Complimentary or discounted rooms, food, spa treatments, and transportation are just some of the enticements casinos use to lure customers back. The high rollers get anything they want—private jets, limousines, fur coats and jewelry—it's all available if they gamble enough money in the casino. In fact, the highest rollers even get some of their money back —a discount on the money they lost while playing in the casino. Some high rollers who lose a few hundred thousand dollars in one night might receive as much as 30% of their money back.

Originally reserved for only high rollers, this discount on losses is now available to all customers in the form of cash back. Instead of categorizing it as a discount on a loss, the casinos provide a cash back reward or incentive based on the amount of money the customer wagers. Depending on the casino, they can receive anywhere from 10-30% of their losses in cash. Sometimes the cash is available immediately, but most often it's mailed to the customer after they return home, giving them a reason to return to the casino at a later date.

IT Leadership

Innovation comes to the technology environment through vision. Applicability comes through executing that vision. Rare is the IT leader that possesses both the ability to step back from the daily fire-fighting to create a vision, and the skills to execute that vision. Successful leaders in today's casino information technology environment must be able to do both.

There are some IT leaders that have the rare mix of both talents — the ability to visualize a new solution and its components and at the same time understand the requirements to build and deploy the solution. People like Glenn Bonner (CIO of MGM Mirage), Bob Conover (CIO at Caesars Entertainment), Marshall Andrew (VP of IT at Station Casinos, (Tim Stanley (CIO of Harrah's Entertainment), and a few others have long been recognized for their vision and the solutions they have created. Their ability to visualize solutions and successfully implement them has a direct impact on their company's performance, and subsequently, shareholder value.

The gaming industry is unique and unlike any other industry. When people say, "It's the same as in manufacturing, we're just selling entertainment instead of widgets," they do not understand the gaming industry. It's very different from any other industry, which complicates many of the tasks that are simple for other companies. What other industry presents an environment that requires a similar level of personalization? The vast amounts of data about a customer's activ-

Lodging Management Systems (LMS)

Established in 1981, Inter-American Data (IAD) is a software developer and leading reseller of IBM iSeries servers and related equipment. The IAD Property Management System is a preferred property management software for world class hotels, resorts, and casinos. Unequaled in reliability and accountability, LMS is the 'cutting edge' in the Property Management Software industry. Powering the largest destination resorts in the world, LMS is also ideal for mid-sized hotels and multi-property management. LMS is an integrated software solution for hotel front office, accounting, and housekeeping operations, resulting in improved guest service. A versatile foundation, LMS allows for the integration of additional modules from IAD or other vendors.

Lodging Management System (LMS) is recognized as one of the hospitality industry's premiere property management software solutions. LMS automates every aspect of hotel operations — from reservations and credit card processing to accounting and housekeeping. LMS also links customers' gaming accounts to hotel accounts and is built on a platform that runs 24/7, so the software is always up and running. Its versatile foundation easily expands to incorporate additional modules for activities scheduling, attraction ticketing, food and beverage, itinerary planning, online reservations, remote check-in, sales and catering, spa scheduling and more.

The latest version of LMS features a graphical user interface that makes it simple to learn and easy to use. The web-enabled system is based on a services-oriented architectural framework that offers maximum flexibility and minimal upkeep.

ity that are used to create custom-tailored promotions for individual players are quite astounding. Key factors such as the player's age, marital status, distance from the casino, wager amounts, casino games played, entertainment preferences, comp preferences, and a myriad of other attributes can all become part of the marketing formula. Some campaigns can be targeted to a large customer segment consisting of thousands of individuals, while others can be so refined that they target just a few or even one single customer.

While some gaming companies are still in the dark ages, viewing IT as "a necessary evil," many others are giving it the attention it requires in the form of resources, money, and most importantly, talented leadership. Harrah's Entertainment is working to maintain its leading IT initiatives with the likes of Tim Stanley, their CIO. Stanley is working hard at continuing Harrah's innovative leadership in the industry, rather than coasting on their existing solutions, by bringing fresh new ideas to IT and the company at large.

Under the Covers

Today's casinos have more systems from more vendors than ever before. Some of these vendors and the technology they use are not always apparent to or consciously thought of by the public. For example, the technology that is used by slot machines to accept and validate currency is not something that average customers may think about when they play a slot machine. But after this technology was developed and deployed in the 1980's by JCM, it revolutionized the way customers played slot machines and the way casinos collected money.

Before these "bill acceptors" were installed in slot machines, customers would need to track down a change attendant and exchange money for a roll of quarters or dollar tokens. The customer then found a machine, broke open the roll, and started to play. And play meant the customer would have to drop one to three coins into the slot machine and pull the handle (or push the button if you had one of the newer slot machine models). To play a different slot machine, customers would have to gather up all their coins in a small plastic bucket and move to a new slot machine.

Bill acceptors changed the way customers played slots: they could insert their currency directly into the slot machine. Changing to a different slot machine still required cashing out of all remaining coins — at least until ticket printing became more popular. The advent of bill acceptors and ultimately ticket printers/validators dramatically increased revenues for casinos, as the rate of play substantially increased. It also decreased operating costs by reducing the amount of coins that needed to be collected, weighed and wrapped from slot machines. In fact, casinos that are 100% ticket-in/ticket-out such as the Borgata in Atlantic City, have been able to completely eliminate the hard count department, reducing staff and equipment requirements.

Another technology key to the slot machines of today is touch screens. Touch screens are used extensively for video poker machines and on some bonus screens for spinning reel machines. The dominant technology used is ClearTek™, a division of 3M Touch Systems. ClearTek™ was introduced in 1994 and acquired by 3M in 2001. Part of the distributive success of ClearTek™ happened through the expansion of VLT's. Required by video machines to select cards, the technology was necessary to provide an effective interaction with customers.

Utilizing Technology to Increase Profit Margins

Technology has always played a role in the business of increasing revenues and decreasing costs, and casinos are no exception. One of the most popular tools used to enhance the slot playing experience for customers is random bonuses. The act of providing random bonuses to slot players can be accomplished in many ways, including paying a large bonus to one lucky player and a smaller bonus to other players in the same area or on the same row of slot machines.

Another very popular bonus is the Jumbo Jackpot, offered exclusively by Station Casinos. Station owns nine casinos in the Las Vegas area and continues to expand their presence both in Las Vegas and around the United States. Currently, Station Casinos owns more than 80% of all the slot machines in Las Vegas. The Jumbo Jackpot is unique to Station Casinos and has clearly provided a competitive edge for the company. Each casino in the Station Casino portfolio has a property specific jackpot which is guaranteed to hit before reaching $150,000. Adding to the excitement, each Station casino displays the current value of all the Station casino's jackpot amounts. This allows players to "chase" the jackpot that's most likely to hit next, the one closest to $150,000. This ingenious new jackpot bonus program has helped create a loyal following for the Jumbo Jackpots, translating into increased revenues for Station Casinos.

Station's Fiesta Henderson

Station Casinos CIO Marshall Andrew along with senior management have quickly realized the power of technology and how it can affect their ability to market to their customers. By designing and building some of the most popular casino hotels in the Las Vegas area, Station Casinos can now attract both locals and tourists to their casinos — and creating the best marketing program for a wide variety of diverse customer segments is a problem only sophisticated technology can solve.

"21" IN THE WORLD
LAS VEGAS
Golden Goose
Fremont
MINT

VIII

Marketing and Technology

NIGHTTIME IN LAS VEGAS, 1980'S

Marketing Execution

In the early days of Las Vegas, marketing was very different than it is today; casino hosts knew most of the real players and handled their every need personally. The customer file for a casino was probably kept on index cards and only used for invitations to special events and New Year's Eve parties.

As the casinos grew in size, the number of customers increased and casinos needed computers to track the thousands of players. Casino hosts still tended to a player's every need, but couldn't provide the same level of personal touch to every customer. So casinos were faced with a decision: either hire enough staff to provide a suitable experience for every customer or install computer systems to allow fewer employees to manage the higher number of customers. This was the foundation for the business model of casino marketing as we know it.

Today, casinos track millions of customers, as many as 30 million for some gaming corporations with many casino properties. It would be physically impossible for human beings to manage these kinds of numbers. Think of the daunting task of tracking all the individual transactions of those customers, numbering in the billions – many computer systems even find it a daunting task. But it is a critical component to the marketing and ultimate success of any casino.

As the sheer number of customers in the casino's database grew each year, more and more advanced computer systems were needed to process the data. Faster microchips, larger storage capacity, and more sophisticated software were developed each year, sometimes a few times a year, in an effort to keep pace with the demands of the gaming industry. Fortunately, casinos were not the only businesses experiencing these growing pains, so extensive resources, both financial and human, were dedicated to the research and development of new technologies.

In a relatively short period of time, we have witnessed an era with relatively little or no computer technology evolve into a world where web-enabled applications are intuitive and allow people to work faster and smarter in casinos. But even though this was accomplished in the gaming industry in a mere three decades, it was still a long road.

Migrating from the simplest form of direct marketing, gaming systems soon offered casinos the ability to track, report, and select customers based on the amount of money they wagered, actually lost, or theoretically lost. They could also factor in things like how often they visited the casino, how far they lived from the casino, their age, and a host of other attributes. This was a big leap for the casinos, allowing the marketing executives to focus their campaigns on specific customer segments as opposed to a shotgun approach that targeted almost every customer.

In an effort to maximize their marketing efforts and minimize their costs, casinos worked to further refine their campaigns by creating smaller customer segments. Sophisticated casino systems provided more flexibility in selecting attributes and managing lists after customers were mailed a marketing offer. But casinos soon realized that for the really big tasks, they needed software that was specifically designed to provide more than just list management functionality. They needed software that could provide a complete view of the customer's activity and subsequently their net worth to the casino. They needed the ability to conduct advanced analytics to determine which customers were likely to respond to specific offers in an effort to custom tailor marketing campaigns as much as possible, maximizing the return on their investment. They also needed to identify and market to customers that were not self-evident in their profitability, a task only a sophisticated computer system could perform.

Some casinos with the resources of a large and talented IT department, such as Harrah's, Station Casinos, and MGM Mirage, were able to embark on projects to create these systems themselves or in conjunction with a software package. Other casinos, without the depth of in-house resources, selected very sophisticated software applications such as E.piphany, Siebel, and Oracle. But many of these efforts, both the custom in-house approach and the software application approach, have met with mixed results. Almost every major casino has at least one nightmare story of how a lot of time and money was expended on a project that ultimately failed, was shelved, or had to be bailed out with additional resources.

PALACE STATION CASINO

The most common scenario usually goes something like this:

A mid-size casino wants to increase the efficiency of its direct marketing programs: lower cost, higher hit rates, and more revenue. Currently, they create a direct marketing list by entering various criteria into their system. This commonly takes the form of:

> Select all customers who play $1.00 slots, have visited twice in the last six months, generate a theoretical win of $400, and live within 120 miles.

The casino decides to invest in a new marketing system to empower their employees and create more successful direct marketing campaigns. The size of the investment is irrelevant – it could be thousands of dollars or millions of dollars – either way they buy a new software tool to conduct their direct marketing activities. This tool has been acclaimed to produce fantastic results, better targeting, more profits, less cost, etc.

After months, or years, of reviews, demos, evaluations, selection, and implementation, the new software finally arrives. Users are trained, invoices are paid, and the casino fires up the new super tool. Then the marketing department begins to use the tool and creates a direct marketing campaign:

> Select all customers who play $1.00 slots, have visited twice in the last six months, generate a theoretical win of

$400, and live within 120 miles.

It may be hard to believe, but it happens all the time. A company spends all this time and money on a new solution, but the marketing team creates the exact same list as they did before the new software. So basically, the casino just spent a lot of money to do the same thing they used to do, but perhaps faster with better packaging.

The most common reason for this lack of success is in the execution of the marketing business model. The software usually performs exactly as promised – we know that computers do what they are programmed to do – it is the human factor that fails to use the technology effectively.

Try as they may with extensive training, expensive consultants, and lots of manuals, there seems to be a high rate of failure in the implementation of these marketing systems. So much so, that the term Customer Relationship Management (CRM) has become taboo in the gaming industry (and many others for the same reasons). But the reason for these failed implementations is not around the installation of the application software – rather, it is the integration of the software into the business model of the casino. A casino should never have to completely turn its back on the way it has always done business in order to use some new software effectively. But by the same token, it can't expect to enjoy the fruits of increased efficiency without making some changes.

There must be a balance between retaining the core competencies of conducting business in a way that has made a casino property successful and making the changes that can improve their effectiveness. The means to strike this balance is in the execution of their business model – a way of examining the step-by-step process for each marketing activity and focusing on execution excellence. Technology may be able to provide a function that was previously unavailable, but more likely it will provide the tools to allow the marketing team to execute faster, more precisely, and with greater results. This comes from the refinement of the business model to exploit the advantages of the marketing systems while at the same time synchronizing the processes.

New Business Model

Computerized player tracking gave casino marketers more data about their customers. They could then use this data to develop promotions to entice players to return to the casino more often, wager more money, and spend more time in the casino when they visited. But it was essential to make sure they didn't expend costly offers without the customers playing in the casino.

What quickly ensued was something of a circus act, where casino operators had to balance comp expenses with attracting and retaining players. Sophisticated computer systems were rapidly developed and deployed to assist in this effort, but many of these systems only complicated the endeavor. So the circus act continued, adding more and more players to complicate things even further. Operating departments added their own accountants and the circus act often became a battle for funds. Eventually, operators (at least the smart ones) came to an understanding about how to effectively offer complimentaries without eroding profit margins.

While casino operators have been tweaking their comp systems and creating new marketing programs, they have been educating their customers (which is not necessarily a bad thing) about how to get the most comps for their play. Remember when casinos thought it was taboo to tell a slot player how many points they needed for a comp? Now customers not only know how many points they need, they also know how much money they need to churn through the slot to earn those points.

This has raised the bar for all casino operators to provide a more robust level of customer service. It's only natural, as other travel and leisure industries have gone down this same path. Hotels and airlines are years ahead of the gaming industry and have increased customer expectations significantly. By not providing some of the same features in casino reward programs, the pitfalls become painfully obvious to the customers (and the casinos!). Not being able to combine points from multiple properties of the same company is just one example.

As technology continues to progress at a blinding pace, thanks largely to the Internet and its underlying architecture, the next chapter in this never-ending story has already been revealed. Some casino operators, such as Mohegan Sun, allow players to redeem points for anything in the casino – including rooms, food, gift shop items, and entertainment. This is clearly where the industry is heading, especially since the operators have finally figured out that one player card for multiple properties makes sense.

Casino Comps

The gaming industry was built on rewarding players to entice continued play and additional trips to the casino. All of the marketing efforts focus on rewarding and enticing players with free or discounted items. Providing free rooms, dinners, limousines, gifts, shows (the list goes on and on) is the casino's strongest marketing tool. However, determining the amount to give back to players is a highly regulated process that is half science and half art.

All casino comps are based on a player's theoretical win. A player's theoretical win is the amount of money that the casino will "theoretically" win from the player. The calculation for theoretical win is based on the amount the player wagers on each decision, the length of time he or she plays, and the casino win percentage of the game being played. There are a few other factors that can be included in this formula to provide a more accurate result, such as the player's skill level or the types of bets being made.

For example, a player that is wagering $100 per hand of twenty-one and plays for eight hours would "theoretically" lose (the casino would "theoretically" win) $308:

$100 wager x 8 hours x 60 decisions/hr x .0214 (casino win percentage for blackjack) = $308 theoretical win

Of this amount, casinos typically provide approximately 30% back to the customer in the form of comps and cash. Sometimes cash is awarded in addition to the comps, but usually this comp amount is divided up into cash and comps:

$308 theoretical win x 30% = $91 comp dollars/points

This $91 dollars or points (casinos may call it one or the other) can be provided in any form or combination of forms, such as half in cash and half in comps. Giving cash back to players has become an important tool for marketing, especially in markets like Atlantic City. Although some casinos give cash back to table games players, the majority of programs focus on the slot player.

What has changed most about cash rewards is how they are provided to the players. In the beginning, cash certificates were mailed to players at their homes in order to generate a trip to the casino. The players would visit the casino, usually stand in a very long line, redeem their certificates and receive cash. There were some variations on this theme, providing paper or coin, etc., but that's how it worked for the most part. The next significant advancement was receiving a coupon with a bar code on it. The player would insert this coupon into a coin vending machine and receive a roll of coins. This still usually required some form of redemption, and losing your coupon, was like losing cash.

Then players started complaining about wanting cash back on the same day. Their argument was, "Hey, I earned it, so I should have it right away!" This required the use of technology to allow players to check their cash balances via a kiosk-type device. Then it would be the same routine – stand in line, redeem, get cash, and go back into the casino. This all seemed like a lot of work for the player – and the operator!

Casinos soon took the next step in how they provided these cash rewards to their customers. Casinos installed kiosks around the casino and near the player club. In the past, players were able to check comps available and print the comp at the kiosk. Soon after, they were able to check cash back balances as well, and receive cash at the kiosk. It worked just like an ATM: the players inserted their card, entered a PIN, and reviewed their balance (both cash and comp). Using a touch screen, the player chose either cash or comps and received a printed comp slip or cash. Except for lines at the kiosks, it was a wonderful way to reduce waiting times and improve customer service.

Some slot system companies took this concept a step further. Advanced Computer Systems Corporation (ACSC), a subsidiary of Bally Gaming and Systems, developed a very sophisticated system that was easy to use. This system allowed players to issue comps and receive cash back right at the slot machine. The cash went right to the credit meter and comp slips printed right at the outlet. That meant that every slot machine was a kiosk, and the player was less likely to walk with the cash, because it went straight to the credit meter!

The more comfortable players become with technology, the more bells and whistles operators and vendors can provide to combine convenience with entertainment, ultimately enhancing the players' overall experience. Companies like ACSC and IGT are continuously working to provide more convenience for casino customers, and new marketing vehicles for the casino operators.

Data Integration

Data Integration, or the act of combining information from different computer systems, has become part of a casino's daily vernacular. As technology continues to permeate almost every aspect of our lives, casino resorts are affected too. Larger casino resorts can have an average of 150 or more different computer systems installed. Much of the information from these systems pertains to customers, and it is essential that people who manage the casinos are able to look at all of the information at the same time.

Casinos, in fact, all companies for that matter, have worked to combine data from different systems in meaningful and useful ways ever since they installed their second software system. They use data warehouses, data marts, downloads, outsourcing, consultants, OLAP (On-line Analytical Processing) applications, and system integrators to try and accomplish the data integration task with varying levels of success.

There are a number of issues to contend with when approaching the data integration challenge, and not all of them are technological. Some are business related, and often are the hardest obstacles to hurdle. The technology exists to extract data, combine it, and store it somewhere, but many casino operators have no idea what to do with this information once they have it on their desktops.

While combining data about financial results is critical to business operations, and sometimes required by law, customer data gets the most attention in gaming. Calculating a true customer profit/loss figure becomes paramount, but elusive. Companies combine data from key systems such as hotel, casino, point-of-sale, spa, reservations, retail, box office, and others, but they usually can't include credit card transactions not charged to a hotel folio or cash transactions, because the data isn't captured and linked to a customer. So they never really know a customer's true value to the casino. The work-around for this little stumbling block is to match credit card numbers to customer data on file (which fails when a different credit card is used) or better, request that customers use their player cards even when buying bottled water in the gift shop. This links all transactions to a particular customer and actually helps to increase membership in a casino's loyalty club as well.

MGM-Mirage Players Club Card

While it is usually easy to overcome platform issues (IBM iSeries and pSeries, Cisco Servers, DB2, SQL, Oracle, etc.) with solutions that talk to everyone and everything, there still remains the task of extracting the data (what data, how much, and how often) and deciding where to put it (data warehouse, data mart, package solution). Companies such as IBM, SRD, TIBCO, and Microsoft are making significant strides in providing solutions that can capture and message this data real-time. These solutions are making it much easier for gaming corporations to access the data they want, quickly and efficiently.

Although casinos can implement the technological solution, much of the industry is still struggling with the most important piece of the solution – the execution. Once technology is implemented, they need to determine how best to use it. Outside of direct marketing, companies can learn much more about their customer segments, growth opportunities, profitable segments and products, and operational improvement opportunities. The market leaders have always known how important data integration is for operating effectively, forecasting, expansion, and growth. They invest the time and money to learn more about their customers so they can make informed decisions about their business.

The Search for the Casino Holy Grail: True Data Integration

The gaming industry looks nothing like it did twenty years ago, and nothing like anyone could have possibly imagined. In 1984, gambling was only permitted in the state of Nevada (sans Boulder City) and in Atlantic City, New Jersey. Since then, many companies have worked to develop custom solutions, customize package solutions, or just dump all the data to Microsoft Access and take their best shot at extracting the data they need in a meaningful way. Yet even today, data integration is still one of the most difficult challenges facing casinos. With so many computer systems playing an integral part of the day-to-day operation of the casino, connecting the systems to each other has become an essential requirement. But because of the disparity between the systems, it is no easy task: different hardware, different operating systems, different data architectures, legacy systems on old technology and new applications running on state-of-the-art technology all contribute to the obstacles standing in the way of integrating these systems. The diagram below illustrates just some of these systems and their integration with each other:

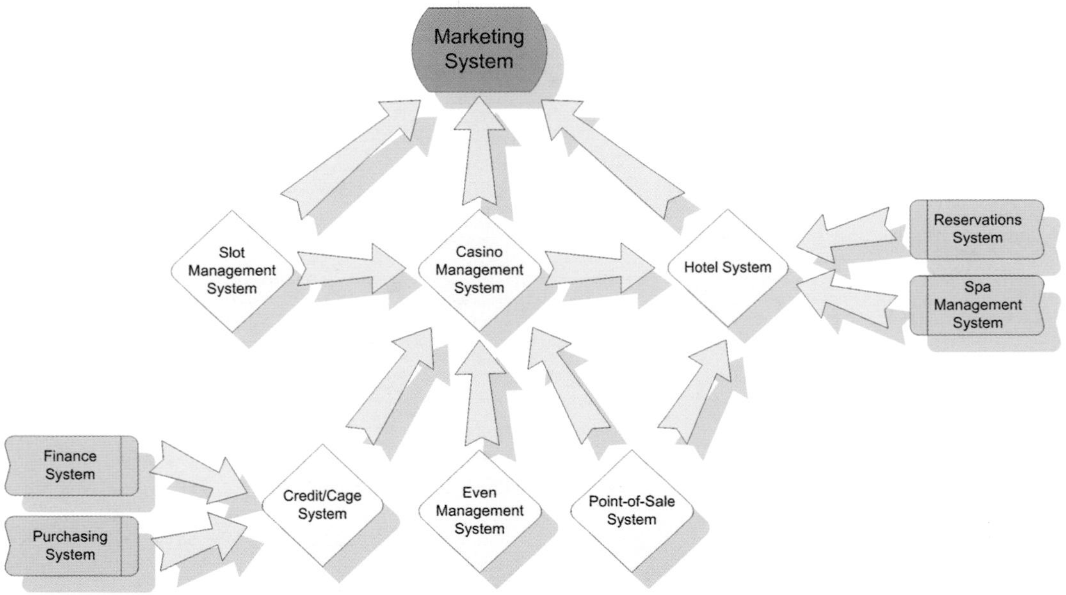

This representation is a mere snapshot of just some of the data files that play a role in a casino resort's data integration challenge. In today's casino resort, there may be upwards of 200 or more information systems, many which contain customer data. Deciding which of those systems hold useful customer data and which ones are less important is a constant source of debate. The valet parking system that photographs the customer's car is not essential to any part of the data integration effort, right? Unless this system is being used to alert someone that this particular customer has arrived on property and a casino host is paged, emailed, voice mailed, or text messaged to meet the customer in the lobby.

So you see, even though technology has greatly advanced during the last twenty years, so has the challenge. The prospect of utilizing Microsoft .NET technologies to integrate some of this data in days, instead of weeks and months (and years for some), is entirely possible. In fact, some gaming corporations have tried this and it works quite nicely. The problems arise when decisions need to be made about what data to integrate (everything, some, or very little), when to integrate (real time, on-demand, batch), where to store it (data warehouse, data mart, cube, flat file, etc.), and most importantly why to integrate the data. Or more specifically what will be done with it when it is finally integrated. There is an excellent argument here, one that plays out on a daily basis: "Our casino has been operating and making record profits every year. Why do we need to spend hundreds of thousands or millions of dollars on a data integration solution?"

Customer Service – A New Marketing Tool for Casinos

The issue facing megaresorts today is how to provide enough attention to customers in order to make them feel special without having to hire droves of employees – and equally important, how to do it cost-effectively.

In amazing contrast to business methods in the U.S., department stores in Asia have a large number of employees stationed throughout the store. You literally cannot walk more than about seven steps without encountering a salesperson. When questioned about this practice, it was determined that this was the level of service that customers had come to expect, and anything less would drive them to a competitor. A stark difference from the cost-saving job cuts and salesperson free zones we often experience (and usually prefer) in the United States.

U.S. casinos must find creative solutions to their customer management challenges. That's where technology bridges the gap. For many years, casinos have used technology to assist in day-to-day management of operations and strategic marketing. But now, resorts are using technology to coalesce data from different sources to create information from the data. Instead of only using this information to conduct tiered marketing campaigns, some companies are starting to transform this information into knowledge.

Providing this knowledge to employees makes them smarter about their customers. It's very similar to intelligence gathering – learning as much as you can about your customers, then using this knowledge to personalize each interaction with the customers. Although this may seem trivial, it actually creates a memorable experience and makes the customer feel special. It also allows employees to work faster because they may already know what the customer is about to request.

The utilization of technology to deliver this knowledge to employees is much more cost effective than hiring, training, and managing large numbers of employees. Although initial capital costs for the IT projects are significant, the benefits are worth the investment, as evidenced by the success of many of the large Strip properties. The challenge is trying to quantify the intangible gains of increased customer loyalty, along with demonstrating that the increased market share and higher revenues are due to customer management and not just casino marketing. Since return on investment (ROI) is always a factor for companies, being able to quantify the impact on revenues or demonstrate cost savings is critical to any technology purchasing decision.

There are two ways casinos utilize this knowledge to increase revenues: on-site interactions and direct marketing. The concept of customer management deals with every interaction while the customer is visiting the resort. Starting with the telephone call to make reservations to the time a customer checks out of the hotel, this knowledge can be used to suggest additional purchases, whether they be room upgrades, entertainment tickets, or retail items. And when this happens in an interaction that is personalized, there is a greater chance that a customer will increase spending than if he or she were not presented with the cross-sell and up-sell offers.

Applying these same concepts when conducting direct marketing campaigns can have a dramatic effect on the success of a casino's marketing efforts. The technology exists to personalize every offer that is mailed to a customer or prospect, and to focus on trigger points for individual customers instead of segments of hundreds or thousands. Casinos can save money if

Old Harrah's Newspaper Ad

they offer some customers $35 in cash instead of $50 because they know it is enough to drive the trip for those customers. There is also technology available to provide customized offers to customers when they arrive at the resort, further personalizing the experience and building customer loyalty.

Harrah's Total Rewards system has many of the features that have been described here. Their patented system has been very successful and is making a significant contribution to their branding efforts and driving revenue at their properties. There are a number of other major gaming companies with similar systems – systems that are deemed a minimum requirement for competing in today's gaming market.

The proliferation of these systems has been paramount to the success and growth of the gaming industry. They have created a cost-effective means for casinos to reward more of their customers than ever before, enticing them to visit and play more often. The results are palpable – multi-billion dollar megaresorts (and mini-cities) continue to be built on the Strip. The systems have even played a key role in the Indian casinos throughout the U.S., evidenced by the fact that the largest and most profitable casino in the world is Foxwoods Resort in Ledyard, Connecticut, owned by the Mashantucket Pequots. Like the city of Las Vegas, Foxwoods continues to grow on a regular basis – announcing expansion plans that cost more than most casinos cost to build.

Gaming Standards Association

To customers playing to win on a slot machine, the machine itself is all that matters—in addition to the prospect of winning big. But to casino owners and operators, gaming involves much more. To support and manage slot machine play, today's casinos take advantage of the many types of innovative and important gaming equipment and systems available, including currency counters, player-tracking networks, food and beverage systems, property-management systems, and slot machine peripherals such as bill validators, card readers, and ticket printers.

But for all of these pieces to make gaming operations more efficient, cost-effective, targeted, and seamless—and to result in higher revenues—they must all function together and speak the same "language." Clear, open communication between gaming devices and systems is critical to the gaming industry.

Unfortunately, many gaming devices have been developed using proprietary protocols, resulting in almost as many communication languages as gaming device manufacturers. As a result, the various devices and systems are unable to work together without significant and continuous engineering challenges. Until 1996, this lack of interoperability hampered operations and prevented gaming from growing as quickly as other technology-based industries.

PETER DERAEDT, PRESIDENT

In 1996, John Acres, of Acres Gaming, set out to change the industry. At the World Gaming Congress & Expo in Las Vegas, he introduced the idea for competitors to work together to develop open industry standards. The concept caught on, and in May 1998 a group of five manufacturers started an industry trade association called the Gaming Manufacturers Association (GAMMA). The association has now grown to include more than 75 members and affiliates, and changed its name in 2000 to the Gaming Standards Association (GSA). The new name better reflects the group's vision and mission statement, which is to be an international trade association representing gaming manufacturers, suppliers, operators, and regulators.

Today, the association is the gaming industry's leading standards forum. Headquartered in Fremont, Calif., it has an international reach and promotes open gaming standards worldwide. GSA facilitates the identification, definition, development, promotion, and implementation of open standards to enable innovation, education, and communication for the entire gaming industry.

The association's work is bringing increasing benefits to the industry. By enabling numerous pieces of equipment to function together smoothly, open standards allow gaming operators to lower costs and work efficiently while offering them an exit strategy currently unavailable. Open standards also allow operators to receive valuable information that helps them meet customer needs and run their businesses in the best way possible.

Open standards are also benefiting gaming developers and manufacturers. By encouraging competition and leveling the technical playing field, open standards bring costs down and make solutions affordable. They also drive innovation, making gaming a high-growth industry.

GSA gaming standards are developed by member companies working together: manufacturers, operators, regulators, and suppliers. This process results in open standards that incorporate a wide range of ideas and in richer protocols than would be developed by one company or one group alone.

Three new GSA standards, developed after years of collaboration by GSA members, are having a positive impact on the gaming industry. The first, Best of Breed (BOB), is a standardized communication protocol that enables secure communications between gaming devices and gaming systems. After analyzing all the current gaming protocols, GSA developed BOB, which at a minimum encompasses all the protocols' features and hence is called Best of Breed. Based on proven industry technologies such as Ethernet, TCP/IP, and XML, BOB enables slot machines to talk to many different peripherals both within the game and outside. It allows operators/regulators to audit the games more accurately, manage game combinations more efficiently, and provide customers with many more options.

Because BOB permits automatic data transmission of game information to a central database, human error is eliminated as is machine downtime. Because it feeds performance information to the central management system, game offerings can be tuned to match the combinations that are most popular at specific times. BOB also provides the capacity to change one slot game for another on the same machine, so customers can download and play the game they want without having to change machines. This offers a solution to game yield management that was never possible before.

The second protocol, System-to-System, or S2S, allows casino operators to link their various management systems and easily connect them to hospitality and point-of-sale systems. Based on the commonly available technologies TCP/IP, SOAP, XML, and Ethernet, S2S allows gaming operators and system providers to use off-the-shelf network equipment and software rather than build custom interfaces to connect their systems. Using S2S standards, operators are able to measure real-time patron activities: table games, slots, and food and beverage consumption, giving them a true picture of customer value. Developers and manufacturers benefit from S2S because they no longer have to spend countless hours engineering and producing equipment compatibility.

The third protocol, the Gaming Device Standard, or GDS, is a standardized communication protocol that links peripheral devices to a gaming device. Devices such as note validators, coin acceptors, coin hoppers, touchscreens, card readers, and ticket printers all use GDS to talk to the slot machine. GDS enables true plug-and play capability based on the well-known standard interface Universal Serial Bus (USB).

All GSA standards are developed from the ground up and are in sync with one another, offering accurate and complete dataflow from peripheral devices all the way to the back-of-the-house systems. They provide organizations with comprehensive information to maximize efficiency as well as profits.

As the three new protocols are adopted by more manufacturers, suppliers, and operators, they will usher in a dynamic new era of gaming. Operators using BOB will have greater game and system configurability and more control over their operations as well as more game/system uptime. S2S will provide operators with more and better patron information so they can make better business decisions. As a result of seamless system integration, transition costs will significantly decrease and IT staffs will be able to act more strategically rather than constantly be putting out fires. S2S will also make the consolidation of accounting information more efficient and provide operators with the true worth of their customers. Finally, GDS will enable more peripheral choices and streamline peripheral control, service, and diagnostics.

By continuing to promote these and other open industry standards, the Gaming Standards Association is working to make the many existing, cumbersome protocols outdated. By encouraging open standard adoption, the association is working to make gaming operations more efficient, keep development costs down, provide new applications and get them to market more quickly, as well as increase gaming revenues and profits.

William F. Harrah College of Hotel Administration
http://hotel.unlv.edu/

With more than 130,000 hotel rooms, hundreds of restaurants, conventions and trade shows, magnificent entertainment venues, famous retailers from all over the world, and superb recreation facilities, Las Vegas has truly become the world's greatest laboratory for UNLV's William F. Harrah College of Hotel Administration. Our faculty base is significantly enhanced with part-time instructors who come to us from the Las Vegas based properties. What student's education wouldn't be enhanced by listening to the General Manager of the Mandalay Bay or the Tropicana Hotel? What student wouldn't learn a great deal from working as a supervisor in the Bellagio buffet? How could important positive qualities not rub off, as an executive at the Venetian mentored you? And serving as an intern in the Rooms Division of the Four Season's isn't bad duty either.

These opportunities are provided for all of the students in the Harrah Hotel College at UNLV. These enhanced learning opportunities help us achieve a level of quality in our programs that provides students with the means to succeed.

Students in the college are exposed to the breadth of the hospitality and leisure services industry while they are also given the opportunity to specialize in an area of interest. Strong academics coupled with focused internship and mentor programs prepare students to enter and ascend to the highest managerial levels of the growing global hospitality and leisure services industry.

Students also have the benefit of learning from faculty members who are some of the country's leading authorities in their areas of expertise. Our faculty has authored numerous textbooks that are used worldwide by other hospitality programs as well as industry professionals.

In the William F. Harrah College of Hotel Administration our teaching, research and service efforts encompass at least the following areas of interest: foodservice management in a wide variety of venues (including fine dining, quick service, concessions, in-flight, hotels and a wide variety of contract service areas such as schools and hospitals); lodging operations management; catering operations management; casino operations management; timeshare management; sports, entertainment and recreation venue management; beverage and bar operations management; facilities management; meetings, conventions and trade show management; club management; professional golf management; tourism retailing management; recreation (including therapeutic recreation) program development and evaluation. Then considering all of these areas of interest, we teach, do research and provide services that pursues an understanding of the human resources, accounting and financial management, marketing and sales management, supervision and leadership, information technology, labor-management relations, security and legal aspects, and the ethics of all operations, in order that we can be functionally effective managers.

Here in Las Vegas, the concentrated focus of activity in a relatively small geographic area brings into mind quickly all of the related businesses that support our industries. One needs to drive only a block or two off of "the Strip" to see vendors and distributors of all kinds that allow our industries to flourish. There are upholstery repair shops, and window covering and drapery businesses. There are uniform vendors. The trades are represented in every possible mechanical and electrical form. The used equipment and furniture market has a good representation as well. Food, beverage, wine and spirits distributors are abundant. The trade newspaper and publishing businesses are very visible as well.

We wonder when these supporting industries will one day become part of our academic endeavor. Where will we draw the boundaries, or do we need to? Can we educate our students in order that they can gain the understanding necessary to work across a broad variety of fields of interest? As information and knowledge explodes we will have to be able to accomplish this or our educational efforts will fail and our students will be so narrowly educated that they will not be able to serve the industry well. Information technology will play an important role in the pedagogy.

FRANK AND ESTELLA BEAM HALL

We now see a wide variety of university level courses being made available to students solely through asynchronous delivery via the Internet. Students register and take these courses from any location, and at any time they choose. In the future there will be sufficient courses offered in this way so that a student could put together a program of study from a variety of institutions wherein the totality of these courses could be viewed as a degree from some virtual university.

The nature of university educational programs will change dramatically because of what will be available from the Internet. The Harrah Hotel College is no exception. Most of our undergraduate courses are available online and we have an Executive Masters in Hospitality Administration available solely over the Internet. Information technology will continue to have a significant impact on our educational processes far into the foreseeable future.

BARONA VALLEY RANCH RESORT AND CASINO

IX

Indian Casinos and Gaming Technology

In the early and mid-1980's, Indian tribes opened bingo parlors on their reservations. Legislation had been passed that allowed federally recognized Tribes to own and operate bingo parlors, and by 1988 revenues were estimated at around $100 million. Native American Indians were anxious to expand their gaming operations to Class III gaming — full casino gaming that includes slot machines, blackjack, roulette, and other traditional casino games.

The Indian Gaming Regulatory Act created three classes of gaming for Tribal communities. Class I games typically refers to historical tribal games which are played in social settings and are not offered to the public.

BINGO AT FOXWOODS RESORT

Class II games include bingo, lotto, pull-tabs, and other bingo or lotto-type games, as well as non-banked card games, if permitted by the State. Class II was the only form of Tribal gaming allowed for many years, until Tribal nations negotiated compacts with the states that permitted Class III games. Class II games, such as bingo, allowed tribes to begin earning revenues that would eventually be needed to open full service casinos.

After heated litigation and debates between individual States and various Tribes, it was ruled that any casino game that a state could conduct for charity, even if just one night per year, Native American Tribes could operate for profit, everyday of the year.

Class III games are traditional casino games as we know them today, but only as

RIGHT: FOXWOODS RESORT AND CASINO

Potawatomi Casino Exterior in Milwaukee, Wisconsin

permitted by the individual state for charity. If the state does not allow slot machines, then a Tribe cannot operate slot machines in their casino. This was the case at Foxwoods Resort in Connecticut until the Mashantucket Pequots struck a deal with the state: a guaranteed payment of $100 million dollars or ten percent of the slot win, whichever was higher, each year. The state agreed to allow slot machines, and now receives over $150 million each year from Foxwoods.

This broke the gaming industry wide open, with Indian casinos being built throughout the country, providing they were on a Tribal reservation. Most reservations are not located near urban centers, so this brought casino gaming to the backyards of many Americans. Instead of having to travel to Nevada or Atlantic City, most people could drive just a few hours to an Indian casino.

Today, there are over 350 Indian Casinos throughout the United States, reaching from California to Connecticut to Florida. In fact, the world's largest and highest earning casino is Foxwoods Resort and Casino, an Indian casino owned by the Mashantucket Pequots in Ledyard, Connecticut. Foxwoods has over 350 table games, over 7000 slot machines, 2000 hotel rooms, and continues to expand their resort.

Indian casinos need the same technology to manage and operate their facilities as any casino. Unlike many other casinos,

Potawatomi Casino Interior

MORONGO CASINO IN CABAZON, CALIFORNIA

however, Indian casinos are self-regulated based on the rules of the Indian Regulatory Commission (IRC). Critics felt this would not be an effective approach to regulating Indian casinos, but in actuality it has been very successful. Indian casinos have adopted some of the strictest regulatory rules and controls of any gaming jurisdiction, and because they effectively enforce and monitor them, they have created some of the highest integrity operating conditions in the gaming industry.

Indian casinos have often been at the leading edge of technology advancement in the gaming industry. In the states that do not allow slot machines to be operated, Indian casinos were the first to install video lottery terminals (VLT's). Also, the VLT's were often cashless — requiring cash to be exchanged for tickets to be inserted into the machines, and payouts to be printed on tickets — years before casinos in Nevada and New Jersey adopted the technology. Much of the trial and error associated with these technologies was played out in Indian casinos.

Indian Casinos in California Help to Change the Gaming Industry Landscape

Other than Foxwoods in Connecticut, most Indian casinos were small and didn't offer the amenities that a Las Vegas casino would offer. This was primarily because they didn't have the market demand to justify building those types of venues. But in California, many of the Tribal reservations were located in pristine areas, not very far from large populations.

Las Vegas casinos saw the expansion of Indian gaming in California as a threat, and tried to block the state's approval to allow slot machines at the Indian casinos. But the die was cast, and soon after that approval, Indian tribes in California had the vision to build large casino resorts that would compete with the biggest, most luxurious, and most profitable Las Vegas casinos.

As the potential for these developments was realized, financing, management teams, architects, and supply companies were at the ready to work with the Tribes to make their vision a reality.

Some Indian casinos, such as Barona Valley Ranch Resort and Casino in Southern California, took this opportunity to develop new technologies that could be marketed to other casinos. They also worked to create a new marketing system to better market to their customers. Surprisingly, Indian casinos still have not convinced all of their critics that self-regulation works. Even after years of great success, Indian casinos are still attacked by the media for lack of controls, while critics fail to see that the combination of strict regulatory rules and the most advanced technology have led Indian casinos to the forefront of gaming integrity. Indian casinos have adopted rules and regulations that are as strict, or even stricter, than casinos in traditional gaming jurisdictions such as Atlantic City and Las Vegas. In fact, many Indian casinos are required to obtain approval from the same gaming labs (GLI) as many non-Indian casinos.

The Impact of Indian Casinos on Technology Vendors

The pervasive expansion of Indian casinos throughout the United States has helped fuel billions of dollars of economic stimulus. Included in this economic boon is the ancillary benefit to technology vendors. In 2002, there were over 350 Indian casinos employing over 400,000 people, representing approximately 21% of the entire U.S. gaming market, and generating $14.5 billion in revenue. The purpose of Indian casinos is to generate funds to help provide education, health benefits, and employment for Indian peo-

SLOTS AT BARONA VALLEY RANCH

ples throughout the country, and they have made great strides towards their goals. Each Indian casino requires technology solutions similar to those found in Las Vegas style casinos. And the numbers will continue to grow—especially on the revenue side. As more and morc Tribal governments build casinos that rival the best Las Vegas has to offer, their revenues will continue to increase.

The size and complexity of Indian casinos demand the same high-tech solutions to support their hotel, casino, marketing, and food and beverage operations. This need has certainly helped vendors and manufacturers in the gaming industry expand their operations and grow revenues. Some technology companies have even been created as a direct result of Tribal gaming, such as VCAT. VCAT, or Venture Catalysts, created Mariposa, a marketing system designed to help all casinos, not just Indian casinos, maximize their returns on customer investments. Indian casinos have also played an important role in the expansion of Enterprise

The "Tree of Life" at Mohegan Sun

WOMBI ROCK CASINO AT MOHEGAN SUN

Resource Planning (ERP) systems in the gaming industry. While some gaming corporations flirted with the idea of installing these multimillion dollar systems, Foxwoods Resort Casino, the Tribal gaming operation of the Mashantucket Pequots, was the first to commit to a full solution. Foxwoods made the decision to buy and install PeopleSoft, helping to lead the way for PeopleSoft to expand into other gaming companies. This also opened the way for other large scale system providers such as Oracle, SAP, and Siebel to enter this market.

Before the proliferation of Indian casinos in the 1990's, there were only a handful of places in the whole U.S. in which you could gamble: Nevada, Atlantic City, Biloxi, and some riverboats in the Midwest. There were a few racetracks with slot machines, and some Class II gaming operations. (And you couldn't gamble everywhere in Nevada – Boulder City still prohibits casinos to this day, a hold over from the days when Boulder City was a construction camp for the Hoover Dam. At least they lifted the ban on alcohol!).

As Indian casinos started to open across the country, competition for the gaming dollar grew more intense. Many feared the competition would be between the Indian casinos and places like Las Vegas and Atlantic City. But in fact, Indian casinos only served to accelerate the growth of gaming. Many people that had never visited Atlantic City or Las Vegas because it was either too far or just not a priority vacation destination could now visit a casino by hopping in their car and taking a short drive. Many Indian casinos are just one or two hours from major cities with large populations. Once people visit the casinos and enjoy the gaming experience, restaurants, and entertainment, they often decide to visit Las Vegas. This phenomenon has contributed to the continued growth and expansion of Las Vegas. Every time someone says they can't build any more casinos or hotel rooms because they have reached the saturation point, another casino hotel opens or expands and flourishes.

Instead of competing with Las Vegas, the competition grew between Indian casinos and other gaming venues such as riverboats and racetrack casinos. Take for example Foxwoods Resort Casino and Mohegan Sun; two of the largest casinos in the world (Foxwoods boasts the largest casino in the world and the highest casino revenue in the world) that are only about 10 minutes apart. In California, there are over 50 Indian casinos, many very close to each other and competing for the same customers.

This competition has led to the development of new and innovative technologies at Indian casinos. While some of the smaller Indian casinos do not have the most advanced systems (mostly because they don't need them), some of the larger ones have systems that Atlantic City and Las Vegas casinos have not installed, such as CRM solutions and advanced ticket-in, ticket-out systems. Barona Valley Ranch Resort and Casino, a California Indian casino that would match up against any Las Vegas casino, has been leading the way for Indian casinos in cashless gaming, continuing the use of tickets when many thought the way to make more money was to move to slot machines that dropped actual coin.

Tables at Foxwoods Resort Casino

All this competition and growth is the main reason that we see so many more technology vendors in the marketplace, as well as the introduction of companies that have traditionally not targeted the gaming industry. The direct and non-direct impacts of Indian casinos have not only benefited the Tribes and their surrounding communities, they have played a key role in the expansion of gaming technology vendors.

Barona Valley Ranch Resort and Casino
www.barona.com

The Barona Band of Mission Indians is known for its independence, self-reliance, and community values, traits that explain the fascinating success story behind the resort and casino that bears the Tribe's name.

At least twice in the 1990's major casino equipment manufacturers and major Las Vegas casinos attempted to change the slot machine landscape by replacing coins with vouchers. They couldn't make it work. It took former Barona Tribal Chairman Clifford LaChappa, his forward thinking Tribal Council and a Tribe that has always believed that the "destiny of gaming innovation" is their job to do. Ticket-in Ticket-out slot machines were introduced on a property-wide basis at Barona in 2000. Nobody else could perfect the technology, so Barona had to do it themselves. The casino is still unique in its voucher system integration with all other systems, total casino coverage of mobile cashiers with palm PC's and wireless ticket scanners. And its technology pipeline is filled with more innovations, guaranteeing that Barona will remain the technology and operations leader for years to come.

"Contrary to fashion, Barona does not view technology as a means to eliminate paperwork and staff," said Tony DeLeon, president and CEO of Tony DeLeon and Associates. "Of course they look at efficiency, but more importantly they look at how technology, combined with people, can enhance the entire guest experience and therefore revenues."

This focus on the human element is traced to the Barona Tribe. "People are encouraged to treat everyone like family," said Karol Schoen, general manager, Barona Valley Ranch Resort and Casino. "For the Tribe to make this the philosophy of the casino says it all. I have never seen a place, from top to bottom, where people treat each other with as much respect. It is the most amazing casino, and a blessing in this industry."

The history of Barona Valley Ranch and the Tribe's "destiny of gaming innovation" began with Barona's historic U.S. Supreme Court victory in 1982 that opened the first door for

BARONA VALLEY RANCH RESORT AND CASINO

Clifford M. LaChappa, Chairman of The Barona Band of Mission Indians From 1989-2004

gaming on Indian Reservations in California. In 1990, the Barona Tribe approached VCAT's founder Don Speer, who was known for turning troubled businesses into successful enterprises, and asked him to help the Tribe reach their dream; developing the greatest casino in the world.

In the beginning, Barona competed against two other casinos that both had locations far more convenient to the San Diego population than Barona. However, the Barona Tribal Council and the Barona Tribe rolled up their sleeves and went to work on creating a better product that would win customers away from the competition.

"We built a card room in 1992," recalled Speer. "The bingo hall was open, but it was struggling. We built the most gorgeous poker room in California, but we had no customers. Our very first New Year's Eve, we had one customer. We threw a party and no one came."

Barona decided that the way to really win customers over was with our cultural tradition of friendliness and service. Barona spent the next two-and-a-half years practicing how to be polite and honest, and how to maintain the cleanest casino anywhere.

Eventually, the customers showed up to play a Barona invention, a progressive Class II card game called *Jokers Wild 21*. By then, Barona's original 37 staff members were absolute experts in customer service. As Speer puts it, "service had become part of the DNA of the organization."

By 1994, with Kenny Rogers as a celebrity spokesperson, the Tribe opened the Barona Big Top, the first Native American gaming operation to incorporate a theme. The Big Top was an overnight success. Barona quickly became number one in the San Diego market. It was to be one of a string of firsts for the casino. After the California constitution was amended in March of 2000 Barona was the first California casino to receive Las Vegas slot machines and to feature cashless slot machines and handheld wireless ticket scanners. The opening of the Barona Creek Golf Club in January of 2001 also introduced the first golf course in San Diego to be built on Native American land. Then *Golfweek* Magazine ranked Barona Creek as the 3rd best resort course in California, just behind two legends in the golf industry – Pebble Beach and Spyglass Hill.

The change in California law led to creation of the present-day Barona Valley Ranch. Nestled in the tranquil Barona Valley, the $300 million property has 400 deluxe rooms and suites in its luxury hotel, a full-service spa, 300,000-square-foot casino, 2,000 slot machines, nearly 70 gaming tables, a poker room, off-track

Inside the Casino

betting parlor, bingo hall, numerous fine dining establishments and the Barona Creek Golf Club. There are over 3,300 staff members with a total compensation package that exceeds $116 million, compared with the famous 37 staff members back when the Barona Tribe first shared their dreams with Speer. In 2001, the casino was named the most progressive and technologically advanced casino in America by the *Las Vegas Investment Advisor*.

El Capitan Grande Suite Living Room

El Capitan Grande Suite Bedroom

Barona's cashless voucher system was at the heart of that designation. Prior to the year 2000, the casino had 1,057 ticket-out only machines. Like every other tribal property in the state, Barona was prohibited up until then from operating gaming machines that dispensed coins. The other operators in the state thought that coin-operated machines were the future. But not Barona.

"When the law changed, we had already determined that coin games were yesterday's product and players preferred vouchers for their ease-of-play and convenience," said Nick Dillon, executive director of casino operations at the Barona Valley Ranch Resort and Casino. This conclusion was confirmed in early 2000, when Barona took three different junkets of its best players to Las Vegas, supplied them with lots of cash and let them play the machines. As part of the deal, they participated in a focus group at the end of each day. Toting coins around in buckets, waiting for the all-too-frequent hopper fills, and dealing with lines at the cashier window turned out to be less appealing than anticipated.

"The bottom line was they went in there thinking, 'I can't wait to play coin machines,' and came out saying, 'I hate coin machines,'" said Linda Devine, assistant general manager of sales and marketing for the Barona Valley Ranch Resort and Casino. "We were hoping they would react that way, because we saw vouchers as one of the steps into the future."

Determined to go with a 100% voucher-based system, Barona still faced challenges. They demanded that tickets work across different platforms, meaning that a ticket printed from one manufacturer's machine could be inserted into another's like cash. In 2000, this was a revolutionary idea. The voucher system also had to mesh with Barona's slot accounting system. And the casino insisted that players not be forced to go to the cashier cage every time they wished to redeem a ticket.

Working with its existing systems provider Sierra Design Group (SDG), slot accounting and player tracking provider Bally Gaming and International Game Technology (IGT), Barona devised the most advanced voucher-based gaming system ever known.

"We were virtually 100% cross-platform when we started out," said Dillon. "No other system supported what we had when we developed it. And no other operator has embraced what we've done 100%. Our voucher and cashiering program interfaces with our slot system, our casino system, and our Mariposa data warehouse. So there's real-time communication with the slot machines for redeeming and issuing tickets. With that, we added wireless cashier terminals-used by cashiers roaming around the floor-that talk directly to our database."

Because of Barona, Ticket-in Ticket-out is a mainstay in almost all casinos now, but mobile cashiers, as the primary source of redemption, is still unique to Barona. The mobile cashiers, who validate the tickets with scanners and hand-pay cash to players, add convenience and one-on-one service to the player experience.

"We'll have 55 customer service cashiers on the floor with palm pilots just cranking on a Saturday night," added Dillon. "It's amazing to watch."

Barona's innovations continue to this day. Working with SDG, it has developed a cashless system for high-end players. The Biometric-enabled system allows players with deposited funds on account to identify themselves with their fingerprint on a slot machine touch screen. They can then transfer their money into the machine via electronic funds transfer (EFT), and deposit any winnings back into their account. The technology spares big players from loading scores of hundred-dollar bills into a slot machine for just a few spins.

The system also processes W-2G tax forms for jackpots $1,200 or higher in real time, without interrupting play. Premium players, who routinely wager $2,000 per spin, can get a pay-out over $1,200 when they do something as trivial as line up two cherries. Barona's technology enables the casino to unlock the machine remotely, and to track the W-2G's. All of these Barona innovations give premium players an interruption-free casino experience.

WINNERS ROUNDUP

The property has also developed a touch-screen player interface called the "Barona Player Loyalty Program." A seven-inch touch-screen embedded in the belly-glass of the slot machine allows players to interact with the casino system, enabling them to do such things as look at their status in the players club, order food and drinks, and register for promotions.

True to the Tribe's penchant for getting things done on its own, Barona's innovations are generated in-house, with the help of an IT department that numbers 60 professionals—unheard of for a single property operator. And Barona was also the first in the industry to implement Mariposa Software, a comprehensive casino CRM software suite developed by VCAT that significantly maximizes casino revenue. (See related VCAT profile).

It's safe to say there isn't a bigger thinking, more influential independent casino operator on the planet than Barona. And, there is much more on the drawing board. (Can you say "Server Based Gaming")?

Venture Catalyst Incorporated

www.vcat.com

www.mariposa-software.com

Those who have been around the casino industry awhile like to remind us about the good old days, the "Golden Age" of Las Vegas. Don Speer talks about those times in the context of customer relationship management (CRM).

Speer, the Chairman of Venture Catalyst Inc. (VCAT), characterizes that period as a time "when the customers were looked upon as our most precious assets." But Speer is not content to merely reminisce about the past; he has transported the important parts of yesterday to the Barona Valley Ranch Resort and Casino and energized the whole experiment with the industry's most innovative customer service technology. Under his leadership, VCAT has managed to keep their clients, and most importantly the Barona Tribe, with one foot in the service-oriented Golden Age of gaming and the other on the leading edge of technology. It's an approach that has produced remarkable results at the record-breaking and award-winning Barona Valley Ranch Resort and Casino.

This has also resulted in the creation of Mariposa®, a CRM software package that VCAT markets to casinos everywhere. Mariposa brings data management capabilities to independent casino operators that even the biggest companies don't have. The program is in many ways a reflection of the VCAT team, which understands first-hand the benefits of corporate casino discipline and the realities of properties with large customer bases and lean marketing structures.

BARONA VALLEY RANCH RESORT AND CASINO, SAN DIEGO, CALIFORNIA

"By definition, casinos are marketing companies, but unfortunately most haven't had the opportunity or capability to develop the marketing structures needed to realize their potential," said Greg Shay, president and CEO of VCAT.

Mariposa was developed by VCAT for Barona, a casino that attracts and retains customers through a nimble combination of technical solutions and the personal touch. With over 500,000 players in its database, 2,000 machines on its slot floor, and nearly 70 table games, technology is an essential tool to CRM at Barona. More than a dozen other gaming resorts, including the Hard Rock Hotel and Casino in Las Vegas, are about to knock the ball out of the park with Mariposa.

"Using a desktop computer or a hand-held device, we can identify a customer, find the slot machine she is playing, know that her husband's name is Frank and she has two children and most importantly her value to the casino and which offers she accepts as well as any offers she has received and hasn't yet accepted," said Shay. "There are many ways that technology can bridge gaps and make that human experience more robust for more people and Mariposa is the best tool to accomplish this."

To explain the power of Mariposa, Shay uses a mythical customer named "Marge," who has two different types of experiences. One at a casino without Mariposa and another at the Barona Valley Ranch with Mariposa.

In the first instance, Marge visits a casino for the first time. She signs up for the players card, plays for about an hour-and-a-half, and loses. It's a very uninspiring, but typical, first-time player experience. She leaves without any direct contact from the casino, and ends up in the slot player database. In a couple of weeks, she gets a letter from the casino saying, "Thank you very much. We'd love for you to come back. Here are some of the amenities offered to the club's members." "Sort of a typical interaction," said Shay.

In the second case, Marge goes to Barona with Mariposa software as an accompanying service strategy in place. She signs up for the player's card, plays for about an hour-and-a-half, loses, and she leaves.

But this time Mariposa categorized Marge as a potential high-worth player. And that was done because Mariposa's powerful predictive modeling tool has analyzed every one of Barona's top-tier customer's first trip, and Marge fits into the model of a potential high-worth customer, one who averages $500 a trip instead of her $70 trial visit. It then calculates her lifetime value to Barona. Why? Because she played fewer than three machines, she lives less than 50 miles from the property, her first buy-in was with a $100 bill, not twenties, plus many more important characteristics. Because all those behaviors are indicative of a high-worth customer, modeled from the property's entire database, Marge is in a potential high-worth category.

Her experience, as a result, will completely change from that uninspired version because this time the casino is on "Marge Alert." She'll be assigned a host who will find her on the floor as soon as she sits down, using Mariposa's Data Visualization Module which provides visual depictions of casino floor activity, as it happens. She will be sent a personalized robust offer that fits her value perfectly and will hopefully bring her back within the next week to 10 days—probably a free play offer, a food offer and an offer to stay in a hotel room are included.

When she comes back to redeem any of these offers, as soon as she puts her card into a slot machine or sits down at a 21 table, a host somewhere at a desktop computer will receive a message: "Marge, a new customer that has been assigned to you, is here playing and has never been contacted by you. So you need to go out there, talk to Marge, and establish that one-to-one relationship." The host will introduce himself to Marge, and tell her that he's in charge of her experience from now on, and that he really wants to make sure that Barona Valley Ranch Resort and Casino becomes her casino of choice.

He'll also extend another invitation; say to a planned barbecue for high-worth customers in two weeks. He'll say he'd really like Marge to

JAVIER SAENZ, DON SPEER AND GREG SHAY

go with a friend. Marge replies that her husband Richard likes 21 (which the host enters into Mariposa seamlessly, plus any other information Marge gives him). From that point on all of Richard and Marge's data is part of the arsenal of information that is available to that host to create one-to-one relationships.

The host leaves Marge and notes in the hand-held computer to call Marge in a week to ensure that she comes to the barbecue event. The whole experience is now programmed so that both sides can get the benefit of a one-to-one relationship.

"How many thousands and thousands of Marge's are out there?" said Shay. "How many thousands have already been to a particular casino and the casino has no idea how much they are missing by not identifying Marge as a potential high-value customer? How many thousands and thousands of dollars is Marge worth in a lifetime? You do the math," said Shay.

Mariposa is the brainchild of Javier Saenz, VCAT's senior vice president, information solutions. A veteran of Harrah's Entertainment, Saenz has held such wide-ranging positions as financial analyst, database analyst, executive casino host, and database marketer, where he was responsible for extracting data from the database, identifying target customers and mailing offers to them. Saenz and his team of Mariposa developers have brought Mariposa to a level of excellence never seen in the industry.

"In my past, every time I approached the problems that these jobs presented, I was never given the tools to do them," said Saenz. "It was a very piecemeal, bubble gum and duct tape approach; use the tools that your predecessor developed himself or create your own. There was no enterprise level software package or process management for any of these jobs. It wasn't until I found Don Speer and VCAT that I actually found a champion who enabled me to go out there and build it. Now this tool is available to the entire gaming industry."

Mariposa fills a need for a company with up to five or six casinos, added Saenz. A central theme of the package is autonomy, finally, for the marketing department and very user-friendly ease-of-use. For instance, Mariposa's campaign management module handles all of the technical requirements of creating a campaign so that one user, literally from their desktop, can completely design a direct mail or promotional marketing campaign from beginning to end.

The program addresses segmentation questions, such as, 'who am I going to market to? Do I want to go after my female slot players who tend to play on Tuesday nights? Or do I want to go after the blackjack players who play on the weekend?'

"That process has historically required a great deal of involvement from the IT department," said Saenz. "Your database marketing person says, 'This is who my target is, but I can't get the data out'. They don't have access. They can't write sequel statements and do all the work that's required to get data out of a database. The campaign management system puts this function back in the hands of the marketing department and lets them do it from their desktop by removing IT level technical requirements for getting the data out."

Mariposa also makes the finance job easier; it generates a pro-forma, projecting the performance of specific campaigns. "So, not only don't I have to go after IT for my sequel statements, I don't even have to go to finance to get a pro-forma," said Saenz. "I don't need to explain to a financial analyst what I'm trying to accomplish with this campaign, what the redemption rates are and how to translate that into revenues. The system does that automatically and then sends it to the analyst."

"We've taken the technology and made it transparent to the user. They don't care that there's a sophisticated multi-dimensional data warehouse behind this program. What they know is they can find their female slot players who play on Tuesday nights, and that's what matters to them. That's a big part of what I think technology should always deliver; simplicity."

"And a better experience for the customer," Speer and Shay would no doubt say.

National Indian Gaming Association
www.indiangaming.org

Long before European settlers came to America, gaming was an important part of the Native American culture, particularly tribal ceremonies and celebrations. Today, Indian gaming is a major catalyst of economic growth and development as well as a vehicle for greatly improving the lives of the Indian people.

Tribal government gaming is now a $17 billion industry, and has created more than 500,000 jobs nationwide, for Indians and non-Indians alike. It is one of the few economic development tools that has benefited the Indian nations in over 200 years.

But gaming is not an end in itself. It is a bridge to helping Native Americans strengthen their communities and provide for their people.

The National Indian Gaming Association, or NIGA, is a non-profit trade association that was created to advance the economic, social, and political status of Indian people everywhere. Comprised of 184 American Indian nations and non-associate members, NIGA operates as a clearinghouse and educational, legislative, and public policy resource for tribes, policy makers, and the public concerning Indian gaming issues and tribal community development. NIGA is led by chairman Ernest L. Stevens, Jr., a member of the Oneida tribe of Wisconsin.

POTOWATAMI EXTERIOR - THALDEN ARCHITECTS

NIGA works hand in hand with IGRA, the Indian Gaming Regulatory Act, which was passed by Congress in 1988. The Act recognized the right of Indians to conduct gaming operations on Indian land, and required that all revenues from tribal gaming be used solely for governmental or charitable purposes. Similar to the way state governments use state lottery funds to benefit residents, tribal governments use gaming revenues to benefit Native Americans: building and improving houses, schools, roads, and infrastructure systems; providing health care, education, and scholarships; supporting tribal courts and law enforcement; and developing a strong economic base.

Currently, Indians living on reservations, most of which are in remote, inconvenient areas, are at the bottom of nearly every economic category. More than 30 percent of the country's Indians live in poverty—the highest rate of any U.S. ethnic group—and the employment rate for Indians living on reservations is 45 percent; some tribes have unemployment rates as high as 80 percent. But even those who have jobs often earn very little—according to the Bureau of Indian Affairs, only 28 percent earn more than $7,000 a year. With the many economic, health, and other issues they face, the life expectancy of Native

Americans is only 47 years.

While not an answer to every problem, Indian gaming holds great hope for reducing Indian poverty and enabling tribal members to enjoy an improved way of life. Proceeds from gaming have already generated more revenue and produced more positive results than any federal stimulus effort ever has before.

But Indian gaming does not benefit only Native American tribes. Gaming is making large and growing contributions to economic growth in a number of states. In California, for example, Indian gaming produces more than $120 million in state and local taxes annually. It also generates more than $1.5 billion in casino revenues and has created 140,000 jobs. In Minnesota, Indian gaming is the state's seventh largest employer, and has created more than 30,000 new jobs, three-fourths of which are held by non-Indians. Indian casinos are also the second most popular attraction in the state. In Connecticut, a single Indian gaming facility provides more revenues to the state than the largest corporate taxpayer, one of the country's biggest defense contractors. In all states where there is Indian gaming, direct expenditures by casino patrons lead to expenditures outside the casinos, for goods and services such as lodging, transportation, and meals; to local businesses hiring more employees; and to millions spent on construction and maintenance.

Because gaming has become such an important source of revenues, the Indian tribes, as governments, work hard to ensure their operations' integrity. Three separate bodies oversee regulatory compliance. The first is the tribes themselves. With the passage of the Indian Gaming Regulatory Act, tribal nations were mandated to establish a regulatory body that would make certain that operations were in compliance with local ordinances and state compacts. The Tribal Regulators and Commissions organization now ensures that that is the case.

The second regulatory body is the State Gaming Department. The Department oversees those areas that have been negotiated with the tribes in state or tribal compacts.

The third agency is the National Indian Gaming Commission, which was created in February 1993. The Commission oversees the regulation of all Indian gaming. Additional oversight bodies include the federal government, the Department of Justice, the FBI, and the Bureau of Indian Affairs.

POTOWATAMI INTERIOR

With its operations carefully monitored and its benefits becoming more and more visible, for non-Indians as well as Indians, Indian gaming has become an integral component of tribal economies as well as the means for achieving self-sufficiency—because of the growth and success of gaming, many Indians and non-Indians have been able to get off the welfare rolls and support themselves for the first time. Adequate housing, improved and expanded social services, and needed treatment programs are also more available.

Indian gaming has also resulted in two other important achievements for the Indian people as a whole: new skills and renewed hope. The operation of casinos and the influx of gaming revenues have provided education and training that have deepened and expanded skills, increasing employee value. They have also encouraged many tribes to build on the success of gaming by diversifying their holdings and investing in additional businesses for their future economic stability. The many benefits gaming has provided are helping to assure not only current tribe members' futures but that of their children and their culture as well.

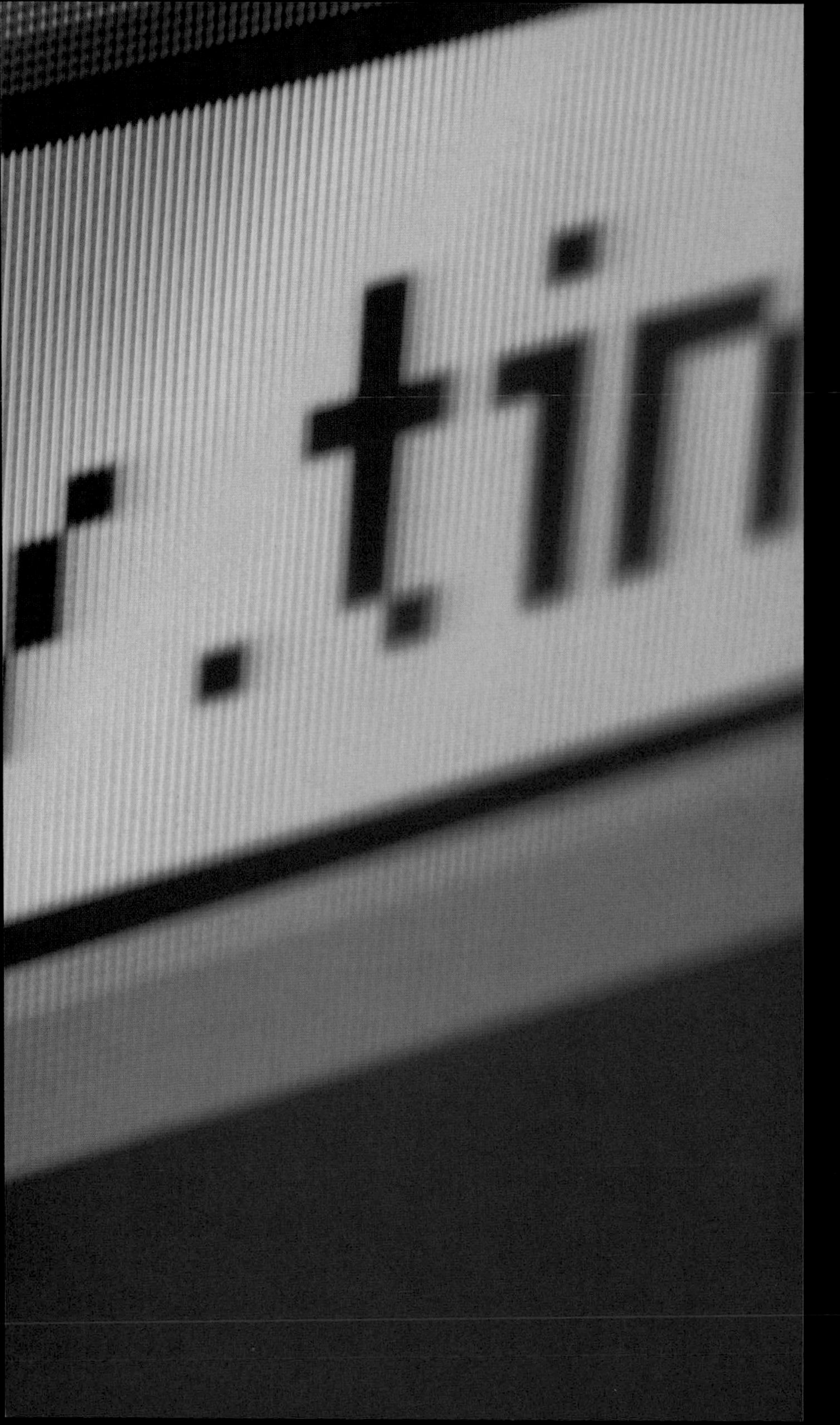

X

Casinos and the Internet

Internet Casinos: Legal or Illegal?

Just like the Boy Scouts with their motto "Be prepared," Las Vegas casino operators are quick to be ready for changes in market trends, legislation, and technology. Changes in legislation will always provide new opportunities for gaming companies, but the trick is knowing how much to invest and when. Invest too much too early, and you might lose your entire investment if the legislation never gets approved. Invest too late, and you lose your competitive advantage and may never catch up.

The pervasive use of the Internet led entrepreneurs to experiment with new ways to offer casino gaming – online. The thought of creating a virtual casino with video slots, blackjack, craps, and all the popular casino games was an attractive lure for technophiles and gaming corporations alike. They imagined the possibilities: reaching literally millions of customers with almost no overhead! The cost to build a casino and staff is hundreds of millions of dollars. A modern casino resort can cost developers from a few hundred million to over a billion dollars to build, and it requires thousands of employees to operate. And even the largest casinos can only service fewer than ten thousand customers simultaneously. But a virtual casino might cost only one to three million to build, or even less – and it can be operated and staffed by as few as fifteen people! There is just one small problem: Internet gambling is illegal in the United States.

PRICEWATERHOUSECOOPERS FACILITIES IN SAN JOSE, CALIFORNIA

It is illegal to own or operate an Internet casino within the U.S., and, it is illegal for U.S. citizens to place wagers with Internet casinos. At least the legislators thought so. In fact, in the mid-1990's there was much debate about the interpretation of various laws that might apply to Internet gaming, such as the Wire Act of 1961. It became a bit of a grey area for some people, especially those wishing to bet on the Internet, but it was much less a grey area for law enforcement and legislators, interpreting the Wire Act to indeed cover Internet gambling.

In an attempt to give the Internet gaming industry some legitimacy, Microgaming formed a deal with PricewaterhouseCoopers (PwC) to review and report on casino payouts and the authenticity of the games. The only problem was that this deal was struck with PwC in South Africa, not the United States. PricewaterhouseCoopers in South Africa is a completely separate audit firm from the PwC of the U.S., and is not required to report to and seek approval from its U.S. counterparts. This caused a significant rift between the two firms, and drew more attention to the work U.S. audit and consulting firms could provide to off-shore Internet casinos. Finally, all of the Big 5 audit and consulting firms (Deloitte & Touche, KPMG Peat Marwick, PwC, Ernst & Young, and Arthur Andersen) were forced by internal politics to turn down any business related to Internet casinos, including audits, technology design, and development.

Riding the .com Wave of Internet Casinos

Almost immediately after the launch of the first Internet casino, more started to appear everywhere in the world except the United States. In 1996, claiming to be the first Internet casino, Intercasino, began operating and accepting real money online. Other Internet casinos, such as Boss Media and Starnet, began operating in exotic third-world locations willing to license and "regulate" Internet casinos in order to receive lucrative licensing fees. Antigua, Barbuda, and Costa Rica became popular licensing venues for early operators of Internet casinos. Within a couple of years, Internet casinos were offering casino games that looked and felt like the real thing, complete with progressive slot machines, multiple players, and even the ability to chat with other online players. By 1998, Internet gambling revenues were estimated to be over $800 million (U.S.), with about half of the revenues coming from U.S. citizens – all while Senator Jon Kyl (AZ) was making repeated attempts to make Internet gambling explicitly illegal.

Although the legality and future of Internet wagering was still being debated in the U.S., some major gaming corporations remembered their Boy Scout training and got prepared. Many casinos had already provided opportunities for web surfers to play casino games for free, awarding token prizes as well as larger ticket items such as vacations and electronics. But now there was an opportunity for major "bricks and mortar" casinos to enter the Internet casino domain. By 2000, Argentina, Australia, the U.K., and many other countries were either licensing or planning to license operators of Internet casinos. It was estimated that at that time, there were probably over 700 different Internet casinos operating on the World Wide Web.

Being good Boy Scouts, MGM Mirage, Sun International, Isle of Capri Casinos, Station Casinos, and Harrah's

BOULDER STATION HOTEL AND CASINO

Entertainment Group all pursued various forms of Internet casino technology in preparation for the possible legalization of Internet gambling. Most were positioning themselves to be licensed in Isle of Man, U.K., as it was understood that this licensing jurisdiction would be the most comprehensive and therefore acceptable to U.S. regulators. It was essential for U.S. regulators to have confidence in the licensing body of any jurisdiction where a gaming company had an operation, even for the Internet. If U.S. regulators felt that gaming laws or regulations might not be stringent enough to protect the games, the customers, and the employees from potential crimes, they threatened to revoke their U.S. gaming licenses. This threat was difficult to overcome, and when U.S. regulators deemed it to be illegal for U.S. gaming companies to operate an Internet casino, and more specifically, to accept wagers from U.S. citizens, they ultimately canceled their plans to launch casinos or stopped operation of their online casinos altogether. This decision was not made easily, as it is estimated that Internet gambling revenues topped $6 billion in 2003 (just under 10% of the U.S. gaming market) and is on track to double to $12 billion by 2006.

Today, the controversy continues, with Isle of Man now accepting bets from U.S. citizens, even though U.S. legislators still consider it illegal. The U.S. is also being pressured from the World Trade Organization (WTO) to legalize Internet gambling in an effort to support trade with licensing countries. In the meantime, U.S. legislators have passed laws making it illegal for credit card companies based in the United States to do business with Internet casinos. Internet gambling and online casinos will continue to thrive, regardless of the position the U.S. takes – especially since about half of all online wagers still come from U.S. citizens. Much like the illegal bookies that still survive even with the pervasive expansion of legalized sports wagering in Nevada and online, online casinos will also continue to survive. The only question that remains to be answered is whether or not the United States will participate in the regulation of – and subsequent tax revenue from online gambling.

Casino Marketing on the Internet

Most casinos and gaming corporations have a website that provides general information about their properties, entertainment schedules, hotel rooms, dining, and retail. Some websites even provide free gaming (no cash awards) and contests

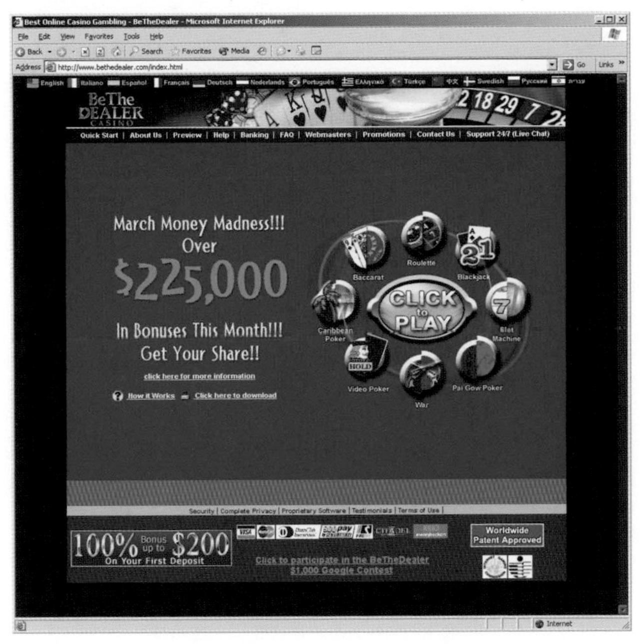

Be The Dealer Online Casino

to win prizes. But we are just scratching the surface with what casinos can learn about and provide to their customers via the Internet.

There are two types of marketing on the Internet: "push" and "pull." The "push" is when things are delivered to you. For example, you receive an email with a room offer from a casino. The "pull" is when you are visiting a website about golf courses and there is a banner advertisement for a casino with a golf course, and it tells you to click for more information – which takes you directly to the casino's web site. Another example of "push technology" is advertising on some news service screen savers that also have links to websites.

You've Got Mail

Many casinos are starting to capture email addresses from their patrons via profile applications they complete while on site or while visiting the casino's website. Casinos are just beginning to execute extensive marketing campaigns via email, because currently only about 20% of customers' email addresses are on file. There are some distinct advantages to be had by conducting email campaigns, but it requires some savvy technology and good marketing strategy.

The cost and time savings alone are considerable motivators to use email more often. Casinos can reach thousands of customers at a fraction of traditional direct mail costs. Also, because email is almost instantaneous (but only as fast as a customer checks his or her email), casinos can use email to fill last minute room vacancies or gaming tournament spots. To be successful, however, casinos still need a marketing system that identifies appropriate customers who are likely to respond to the email.

Casino Websites

Casino websites seem to be in various phases of development. The first generation was very basic information with little or no interaction with the customer – things like the casino address, amenities, etc. The site usually provided static information that changed very rarely. The second generation, where many casinos are now, is allowing customers to make room reservations, buy logo items online, and request additional information. The third generation, where many casinos are going, will allow look-up and review of comp points, redemption for rooms, sign-up for tournaments, and purchase of select entertainment tickets.

HARRAH'S WEBSITE

Gaming companies with sophisticated websites allow customers to enter their player's club card number and password to provide access to their account. Players can review their points, promotional offers, upcoming activities, and much more. Barona Valley Ranch Resort and Casino has taken this concept a step further with a Player's Lounge that is individualized with dynamic content, special offers tailored specifically for that member, as well as a personal messaging system that allows hosts to stay in contact with their customers. The casinos evaluate the customer's profit/loss profile (taking into account the actual value of the customer to the property) and determine which promotions to offer the customer (and how many of each). For example, one customer may be invited to five different slot tournaments, but can only choose one, while other customers may be invited to the same five but can choose three. The same goes for any promotion including rooms, dining, special events, parties, entertainment, etc. Customers can then respond via the website and confirm their reservation in the tournament, room, and even schedule a massage at the spa. Casinos love this interaction with the customer due to the savings from a reduced marketing staff and better customer service. (No telephone calls mean no hold time!).

Your ad here

The next step is for casinos to understand which websites casino Internet savvy customers visit most often and put their advertisement (web link) on that website. There are many ways to gather this information, such as gateways, cookies and portals (e.g., Yahoo!, Alta Vista, Metacrawler, etc.). Just like advertising in the real world, advertising in the virtual world has become very creative, expensive, and competitive.

Corporate Intranets

Many casino hotels are still using a traditional model for employee communication, human resources, and training, but the future of managing these functions is through the corporate intranet. The corporate intranet can process many of these operations, making them faster, more convenient, and cost effective.

In addition to high tech applications like eProcurement and company websites, the same technology can be used to create a corporate intranet in the casino. The intranet is only available to employees via their desktop PC's, strategically placed kiosks, and remote access from home. Unlike the Internet, intranets only allow access by authorized employees with valid security and passwords.

There are many functions that can be supported or enhanced by an intranet including scheduling, benefits, training, and communication. Imagine a web-enabled interface that is personalized for each employee. Let's use a chef for an example:

When the chef logs on to the corporate intranet, he will see many items custom tailored to his use of the casino resort's computer systems. Some of these items may include a schedule, information that he has voicemail messages and email messages – and the ability to listen or read them, an alert that he is running low on lobster, and a letter from the president of the casino.

That alone would be a wealth of information and a level of automation well worth the price of admission. But that is only scratching the surface. From here, he can also review the employee handbook online to check the company policy on vacation time. He can then electronically request time off for vacation, check availability, and assign backup resources. In fact, from here, he can access all benefits information such as 401K contributions and investments, sick days, search for local doctors in his plan, file a benefits claim, apply for tuition reimbursement, and just about any other human resource transaction related to his job.

The corporate intranet will continue to expand its role in the casino resort, saving employees time and saving the casinos money. We can hardly remember what life was like before email and cell phones, and soon, it will be the same with automated employee services.

XI

Security Technology in Today's Casino

Security in today's casino hotels is much more complex than in the days when Bugsy Siegel was building the Flamingo. They're even more complex than the day Steve Wynn opened the Mirage in 1989.

The complexities of the technology, along with the size of new casino hotels, create a challenging environment to secure. Furthering the need for better prevention and faster responses is the constant threat of a terrorist attack, something plaguing all of the United States.

While casino hotels invest millions of dollars to protect their customers and employees, they also spend large sums of money protect-

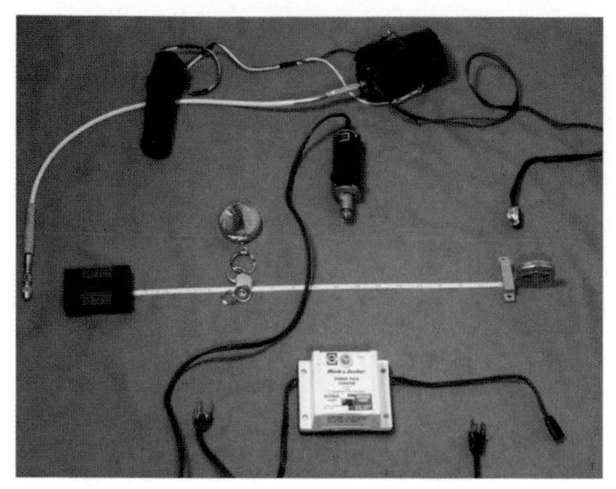

SLOT CHEATING DEVICES

ing the games and data. There is some very advanced technology that is used throughout a casino hotel for security, most of which is unseen to the customer, and to even most employees. From sophisticated fire control systems to video and audio surveillance of all public areas, there is quite an effort to protect guests and employees alike. After the 1980 fire at the MGM in Las Vegas which killed 85 people, Nevada enacted legislation requiring hotels to install smoke detectors and sprinklers in every hotel room. The fire control systems in Nevada also include an audio speaker in the room in order for hotel security to provide instructions for guests in the case of an emergency.

Protecting the Games

Since the effort to rid Las Vegas of organized crime, regulators have gone to great lengths to ensure the integrity of the games that are offered to the public. And as the games, specifically slot machines, started using sophisticated technology like computer chips, they have had to change the way they control and regulate the games.

Protecting the integrity of table games is quite different from protecting slot machines. Since a human is involved in every decision at a table game, it requires a different kind of technology to ensure that the games are not being manipulated to give the house an unfair advantage. Equipment is checked daily to ensure roulette wheels are balanced and not weighted or magnetized, and even the way the dealer plops the ball onto the spinning wheel is watched. (Some veteran roulette dealers practice getting the ball to land in the same number every time – a practice some have perfected and regulators must guard against!). Dice are inspected as well as the cards used in twenty-one and other card games, and just to make sure no one has an opportunity to manipulate the cards or dice, they are destroyed at preset intervals every day or so.

In the 1960's, security and surveillance personnel walked around the casino ceilings on catwalks that were usually equipped with two-way mirrors. This was the most common method to ensure that employees and customers were not cheating the games. Here they could watch any table game or slot machine without the player or dealer knowing they were being watched. But they couldn't watch every game, so it was not a perfect system. The idea that at any time they might be watched was enough to deter most cheating – for awhile.

That all changed when surveillance cameras started to be installed in casinos during the 1970's. Cameras were first

ROULETTE WHEEL

installed to watch the table games, count rooms, and cage areas, but rapidly progressed to watch slots and other areas. It wasn't until advanced surveillance systems were developed and installed in the late 1970's and early 1980's that casinos could watch every camera at the same time, all the time. These systems attached a VCR to every camera, so surveillance teams could concentrate on just a few cameras without worrying about missing something. If there was ever a question about something, they could simply review the tapes from that period of time for a specific area. This dramatically reduced the number of incidents where employees or customers tried to cheat the casino.

While slot machines are under the careful watch of the "eye in the sky" (the common reference to the casino's surveillance cameras), there are still many ways to cheat right in front of the people watching. That's why regulators require authentication of the computer chips installed in each slot machine verifying the win percentage, denomination, and other aspects of the game. This is an important step for regulators, and the way a very innovative criminal was brought to justice. While this is an undocumented story that you wouldn't have heard about on the news, it is rumored to be true:

As the story goes, an employee of one of the big slot manufacturers whose job it was to install the program functions on the computer chips in video poker machines decided to make a little (actually a lot) of extra money for himself. He proceeded to create a program that instructed the video poker slot machine to deal a royal flush after the machine was played in a specific way. After forty times of play where one single coin was entered and all cards originally dealt were discarded, the machine would deal a royal flush. Since the premise of play with video poker is to make your best hand by discarding one or all of your cards, it was nearly impossible that the machine would be played this way by anyone other than his accomplice, and even if it were, it didn't matter because the casino saw it as just a normal part of business. The rumor is that they got away with millions before getting caught.

Protecting the Data

The gaming industry spends an enormous amount of time and money safeguarding their assets and customers. By and large, they do a very good job. But in today's world of viruses, worms, identity theft and terrorist attacks, it has become increasingly more difficult to accomplish this effectively.

While patrons in hotels and casinos enjoy dining, gaming, and sharing personal information with the property, they almost never think about data security – and that's the way it should be. But to create an environment where customers don't think about security because they feel safe requires a lot of work.

There are several ways in which casinos are vulnerable and must protect themselves. Casinos need to protect themselves from disgruntled, mischievous, or criminal employees that seek to defraud, steal, or destroy data. Also, advanced computer systems that are accessed remotely or utilize the Internet are vulnerable to attacks from virtually anywhere in the world.

The personal information contained in casino hotel databases is quite extensive, containing the names, addresses, and sometimes the social security numbers of the customers. Credit players, customers that have applied for credit similar to a credit card application, provide even more information that criminals would be anxious to steal. Years ago, prior to the Internet and remote access to the casino's systems, the problem was more about protecting the data from prying eyes within the casino. Passwords and secured areas usually were enough to deter all but the most determined employees. But once casinos started connecting themselves to the outside world, they opened Pandora's Box – allowing attempts from criminals in far off locations to try to hack into their systems.

It all started when vendors requested remote access to the casino's most sensitive systems, in order to troubleshoot problems from their office locations. While this made sense in practical terms, it did expose a vulnerability to the casinos. Regulators took great pains to delay allowing outside access, but eventually allowed it under tight restrictions. Modems had to be turned on by casino computer room personnel, no incoming calls could be accepted – the casino's computers had to call the vendor, and the modem had to be turned off when the session was over. Sounds great in theory, but it was found that many times the modems were never turned off, and the vendors called in to the casino. Also, as casinos started to connect to sister properties owned by the same parent compa-

ny, vendors found it useful to access a computer system at a single property, then "box hop" to computers in other casinos on their network. Believe it or not, the vendors did this to save money on long distance phone calls!

As soon as casinos launched websites, they opened themselves up to many of the same kinds of attacks we all face today—attempts to access personal data, viruses, denial of service attacks, spyware, and attempts to gain control over a complete network or computer system. The days of innocent hacking by young kids just to see if they could do it are long gone, and now these attacks can be devastating to any company, casinos included. The threats don't always come as a straight on attack — sometimes they can be launched by an employee surfing the Internet and clicking on a website. The next thing you know, the casino can't check people into hotel rooms or the door lock system is not functioning. And it doesn't take long for these thieves to strike. Computer Sciences Corporation (CSC), a leader in Internet security for the U.S. government and corporations, describes how some cyber criminals have programs lurking in the Internet looking for holes to rapidly exploit. A recent such event saw 80,000 social security numbers pirated during an exposure that only lasted 3 hours.

As casino hotels move to create information systems that are more integrated, it creates more exposure. The systems used by casinos, such as Windows, UNIX, and the few proprietary systems still being actively marketed, use the Internet Protocol (called TCP/IP) to provide a common method for computers to talk to one another. The infrastructure of a typical casino uses the same technologies in surveillance, accounting, casino, hotel, marketing, slots, and other operational areas. A security weakness anywhere in the property could be exploited providing access to sensitive data, because everything is increasingly connected.

The attacks of September 11, 2001 have changed the way we approach almost every aspect of our personal and professional lives. And now, as we review our approach to casino hotel security, we find that the physical and electronic security must now be considered together. Investigating an incident of suspected fraud, tampering, inappropriate behavior, or cyber attack now almost always requires the coordinated actions of physical security, surveillance, and cyber security, along with human resources and legal. Each has information about the incident...by pooling the information, rapid response becomes possible and evidence can be properly preserved for prosecution.

Procera Networks
Intelligence Inside Networks

Founded in 2001, Procera Networks, Inc. is a global provider of networking infrastructure equipment. Procera's OptimIP™ family of intelligent network appliances enables businesses to dramatically reduce the total cost associated with networking, security and compliance. With Procera appliances, an enterprise can improve the efficiency of mission-critical applications (QoS), control how and what data is transported through the network, and determine which employees or workgroups can access data or specific applications. Procera's OptimIP™ wire-speed, intelligent network appliances are designed as cost-effective alternatives that can augment and replace multiple server-based products and for quick installation, ease of management and seamless integration with existing network infrastructures and equipment.

Because the Network is your business, you must:

- Ensure application efficiency and quality of service (QoS)
- Eliminate network misuse and bandwidth abuse, and
- Enforce corporate policies and regulatory compliance.

The Procera OptimIP™ product family includes a range of scalable network appliances that provide a comprehensive suite of software applications for secure content management, network optimization, advanced policy-based compliance and selective surveillance. OptimIP appliances are designed for quick installation, ease of management through policy-based control, and seamless integration with existing network infrastructures and equipment. Procera products empower organizations to maximize productivity through intelligent control of the application network infrastructure at a far more selective and granular level than what is possible using conventional network security systems.

Procera OptimIP™ products are based on Procera's IP-Return™ Architecture, which enables wire-speed, deep-packet processing and inspection for Quality of Service, prioritization, optimization, bandwidth management and business-driven control from the user to the application to the network. For today's businesses, information is the lifeblood of the company, and web applications provide a vital yet often-abused window to the world. Network security and performance are essential business assets. Where in past times, the network was the computer, today the network is your business. Procera's OptimIP appliances provide the "intelligence inside networks" that is essential to today's highly functional, compliance-driven and risk-averse organizations.

Years ago, the security and risk management departments were never included in electronic security efforts. Now it's hard to think about doing anything in IT without the involvement of one or both of those departments. According to CSC, surveillance, physical security, and cyber security are coming together to lower cost, close security loopholes, and create a coordinated response. The potentially disastrous threats of the future are so-called "blended threats" — a terrorist attack on the property that is accompanied by a cyber attack, perhaps to disable phone systems or environmental controls or to delay alert and response mechanisms from the first responders.

Casino hotels protect themselves much the same as we do at home. Firewalls, virus protection, and spyware detectors are all employed, albeit more robust versions. In addition, careful procedures are combined with technology and physical security to provide the maximum protection possible. A simple thing such as

changing a password is now paramount to effective security, and changing it once every quarter or even once a month is no longer acceptable. Some passwords are changed every sixty seconds! Users are issued an electronic card key that has a digital display. A six-digit number is displayed which is appended to the user's existing password. This number is synchronized with the host computer, and is updated once every minute. Without possessing the cardkey AND knowing the user's base password, criminals have a tough time bypassing that first level of security.

New Technologies: Advanced Databases, Biometrics, Facial Recognition and More

The technology used to protect casino hotels can hardly be covered in one chapter, but we can provide some interesting highlights, keeping in mind that much of the details are hard to come by on purpose – part of the effort to maintain effective security. The attacks of September 11 have had the most profound affect on security in the casinos. In the past, conducting a background check on casino employees was enough. Today, casinos are starting to conduct checks on customers as well. Systems Research and Design (SRD) provides corporations and casinos with an innovative product called NORA – Non Obvious Relationship Analysis. Part of this product's function is to check employees and customers against a myriad of federal databases, including criminals and terrorist watch lists. The unique feature of this product is that it not only checks the name in the file, but alerts you when the name has a relationship to another name that is in one of the federal databases.

Casinos are also starting to deploy biometrics such as facial recognition, fingerprint verification, and retinal scans to provide access to physical locations, data, or money. As the technology of these devices improves and costs are lowered, it is expected that we will see a biometric security device installed in many places where a key, code, or password is used today.

Some of the most advanced technologies installed in casinos are devices that detect explosives, chemical agents and radiation. While it is known that these detectors have been installed in some casinos, their locations, functionality, and capabilities remain secret in order to maintain the most effective security possible to protect the people, games, and data in the casino.

E R T Y
D F G H

XII

The Future of Technology in Casinos

Downloadable Server-Based Slot Machines

The next step in the ongoing evolution of slot machines and casino gaming is on its way. In fact, it's more a revolution in terms of the effect this slot technology advancement — downloadable games to slot machines — will have on the industry. This gaming format is about to become a hot topic in many gaming circles.

The Client-Server technology supporting this concept is not new to existing network infrastructures. What is new is how it can be used to deliver exciting slot games on the fly to players. Downloadable casino games are already part of the online gaming scene, both as play for cash and play for fun. This technology will provide the ability for a slot player to walk up to a machine and choose the game type and the preferred denomination, and then have that slot game "downloaded" from a game repository on the main server or cluster of servers to the player's slot machine.

For casino operators, the competitive advantages are tremendous. The costs to provide a multitude of games to their patrons are reduced because associated time and labor costs to install these games is eliminated. Historically, machines had to be pulled off the floor and the guts of the machines replaced in order to accomplish this procedure. More recently, computer chips were replaced to update the game configuration, but not without the proper procedures and paperwork being completed, filed, and approved by the appropriate regulators. With downloadable server-based games, casino hold percentages can be changed at any time, even on the fly — with the casino regulators

CYBERVIEW TECHNOLOGY HAS THE ONLY CERTIFIED AND PROVEN DOWNLOADABLE GAMES PLATFORM

blessing, of course. Casino marketers can offer spontaneous bonuses, contests, and special wins at any time. If the belly glass on the slot machine fixture becomes "electronic" as well, signage can be changed or updated as often as the games ("*I Dream of Jeannie*" becomes a "*Wheel of Fortune*" machine as quickly as the network bandwidth allows). The casino floor fixtures and equipment become generic and do not have to be replaced with the games as in the past.

For casino patrons there are pros and cons as well. They can stake out their favorite location on the casino floor, without having to worry if their favorite slot game is located there. Once there, they can simply choose their favorite game. They also can sample new game offerings, or old favorites, via the touch screen format they are accustomed to without giving up their spot with a good cocktail server or near the live entertainment. A player's favorite machine is now wherever he or she wants it to be. The ability to access extensive help screens by touching the screen makes the introduction of new product easier to understand and less intimidating.

The downside to the players is that with this new technology, the casinos will be able to change the hold percentage (the percentage of money the casino wins from the player) whenever they desire. Depending on the regulations that accompany this technology, casino operators might be allowed to make this change without informing the players — they are currently not required to tell them. Imagine a customer playing a slot machine on a busy Saturday night: The casino decides it can afford to tweak the hold percentage up a little bit, earning them a few extra hundred thousand dollars that night. The player may or may not notice that the slot machine they are playing is no longer paying off as frequently as it was just a few minutes ago. If customers are aware of the casino's ability to make these changes, will they revolt and not play the slot machines?

The real challenge in this revolution is in the regulatory arena. Downloading slot games from an out of sight server presents real control risks and a unique challenge. Those charged with policing the process of the movement and administration of the gaming machines in the casino are used to the current level of red tape. If a game is to be replaced, they watch on camera as at least two people, including a security guard, approach a slot machine with the proper completed and submitted paperwork. EPROMS are replaced and the machine now has a new look and feel, and a new hold percentage.

But in this high-tech world of copper and silicon, there is no place for the regulators' cameras. There is also the question of the location of the computer system, and whether it is more appropriate to maintain in the IT computer room or the slot department. There are many issues that remain to be addressed before U.S. regulators approve this technology. Issues such as security, audit trails, testing, game integrity, and functionality all need to be addressed from a customer, operator, and regulator perspective.

The Impact of the Mega-Mergers on Gaming Technology

Like the corporate invasion of the 1970's and 1980's, the merger and acquisition game continued in the 1990's and well past the year 2000. By 2005 there were just a handful of corporations owning many casinos, changing the landscape of the gaming industry yet again. Many fear, as they did when Howard Hughes started buying casinos in the 1970's, that the casinos will lose their personal touch. Casinos have slowly migrated away from the personal touch as the number of hotel rooms grew to the thousands over the years. It was certainly much easier to remember everyone's name, what they liked to drink, and to have their room waiting for them when hotels only had a few hundred people visiting each day. In today's city-sized casino resorts, tens of thousands of customers pass through in a single day.

Technologists and CIO's have long said that technology systems were the answer to the casino managers' prayers. They boasted that new computer systems would allow just a handful of employees to capture, store, and recall minute details about each customer, allowing employees to use this information to create the personal touch that overwhelming size had eliminated. But the delivery of that promise has fallen far short for some casinos. While some gaming companies will embrace this challenge, others will fall further behind in their efforts to personalize the customer experience.

As these great corporations come together to create the world's largest casinos, hotels, and restaurant companies, great care must be taken to craft IT solutions that will make even the biggest hotel casino feel like a private villa. These solutions must work to combine the data and technology resources of the combined companies to create one ubiquitous technology presence with consistent and standard solutions implemented across all properties.

These new gaming giants have the chance to change the customer experience and create a new way of doing business. They can use all of the great resources they will have at their disposal and create something truly unique — a technology solution that will give them a competitive advantage because of the way they have treated the customer instead of the price they charge for their hotel room or because they have the Eiffel Tower in their front yard. These technology solutions can provide the tools for every employee to impact the guest experience by delivering information that is available, useful, and empowering.

Technology has played a role in the gaming industry for decades and has changed the way casinos do business forever. From security to marketing to the slot machines, technology permeates almost every facet of today's casino resorts. Only through the innovative development and creative application of this technology can we enjoy the multi-sensory experiences offered by casinos. As new technologies continue to re-shape our world everyday, so they will in the gaming industry as well.

RIGHT: FLAMINGO 18TH HOLE CLUBHOUSE

Photo Credits

p.8, Las Vegas Convention & Visitors Authority
p.10, Las Vegas Convention & Visitors Authority
p.10, UNLV Libraries
p.11, UNLV Libraries
p.12, White Sand Consulting
p.13, Flamingo Hotel and Resort
p.14, UNLV Libraries
p.15, Flamingo Hotel and Resort
p.16, Flamingo Hotel and Resort
p.17, Flamingo Hotel and Resort
p.17, Flamingo Hotel and Resort
p.18, UNLV Libraries
p.20, UNLV Libraries
p.21, UNLV Libraries
p.22, UNLV Libraries
p.23, UNLV Libraries
p.23, UNLV Libraries
p.24, Boyd Gaming Corporation
p.27, Patrick B. Leen & Thomas C. Nelson
p.30, Boyd Gaming Corporation
p.30, Boyd Gaming Corporation
p.31, Boyd Gaming Corporation
p.31, Boyd Gaming Corporation
p.31, Boyd Gaming Corporation
p.32, UNLV Libraries
p.35, Foxwoods Resort Casino
p.37, UNLV Libraries
p.38, UNLV Libraries
p.42, UNLV Libraries
p.43, Bally Gaming and Systems
p.44, Bally Gaming and Systems
p.45, Bally Gaming and Systems
p.46, Gasser Chair Company
p.47, Gasser Chair Company
p.49, BMM Test Labs
p.50, JCM American Corporation
p.50, JCM American Corporation
p.52, UNLV Libraries
p.54, IGT
p.55, Bally Gaming and Systems
p.56, Bally Gaming and Systems
p.57, Bally Gaming and Systems
p.58, IGT
p.59, IGT
p.60, WMS Gaming
p.61, WMS Gaming
p.62, WMS Gaming
p.63, WMS Gaming
p.64, FutureLogic
p.65, FutureLogic
p.66, MEI
p.66, MEI
p.67, Avero
p.67, Avero
p.68, 3M Touch Systems
p.68, 3M Touch Systems
p.69, 3M Touch Systems
p.70, Caesars Entertainment
p.72, Unknown
p.72, Las Vegas Convention & Visitors Authority
p.73, MGM-Mirage
p.74, UNLV Libraries
p.76, MGM-Mirage
p.76, John McLaughlin
p.77, Venetian
p.78, MGM-Mirage
p.78, MGM-Mirage
p.79, MGM-Mirage
p.80, Harrah's Entertainment
p.81, Harrah's Entertainment
p.82, Harrah's Entertainment
p.84, Caesars Entertainment
p.85, John McLaughlin
p.85, Caesars Entertainment
p.86, IBM
p.88, IBM
p.91, UNLV Libraries
p.92, Tandem
p.94, IBM
p.95, Tandem
p.96, IBM
p.99, UNLV Libraries
p.100, Caesars Entertainment
p.102, InfoGenesis
p.103, InfoGenesis
p.104, WMS Gaming
p.107, Unknown
p.107, Unknown
p.111, Station's Advertising
p.112, UNLV Libraries
p.115, Station's Advertising
p.120, MGM-Mirage
p.121, Keith Costas
p.123, UNLV Libraries
p.124, Gaming Standards Association
p.127, William F. Harrah College of Hotel Administration
p.128, Barona Valley Ranch Resort and Casino
p.130, Foxwoods Resort Casino
p.131, Foxwoods Resort Casino
p.132, Thalden Boyd Architects
p.132, Thalden Boyd Architects
p.133, Thalden Boyd Architects
p.134, Barona Valley Ranch Resort and Casino
p.135, Mohegan Sun
p.136, Mohegan Sun
p.137, Foxwoods Resort Casino
p.138, Barona Valley Ranch Resort and Casino
p.139, Barona Valley Ranch Resort and Casino
p.140, Barona Valley Ranch Resort and Casino
p.140, Barona Valley Ranch Resort and Casino
p.141, Barona Valley Ranch Resort and Casino
p.142, Venture Catalyst
p.144, Venture Catalyst
p.146, Thalden Boyd Architects
p.147, Thalden Boyd Architects
p.148, Photodisc
p.150, PriceWaterhouseCoopers
p.152, Station's Advertising
p.153, bethedealer.com
p.154, Harrah's Entertainment
p.156, Photodisc
p.158, UNLV Libraries
p.159, MGM-Mirage
p.161, Photodisc
p.162, Procera Networks
p.163, Photodisc
p.164, Photodisc
p.166, Cyberview
p.169, Flamingo

Index